A MESSAGE
From the President of the Board of Trustees

It is with great pleasure that the Vancouver Museums and Planetarium Association presents this catalogue of our exhibition of antique musical instruments, *The Look of Music*. The work on the exhibition started some two and a half years ago when a committee of staff and Association members asked the Board of Trustees for approval to stage the exhibition. It was to be the most ambitious and expensive exhibition we had ever undertaken. After extensive planning, approval was given and *The Look of Music* was underway.

We found as we proceeded, as do most others when starting a new undertaking, that not all of the problems were identified and some that were, developed to either a greater or lesser degree than anticipated. The demands on our limited staff were very heavy, but with all of us working together and playing our various roles, the exhibition has come together and is meeting our fullest expectations.

Although this is an exhibition of musical instruments, it and this catalogue are the result of human endeavours from many talented people. Their work would not have happened without the various generous financial contributions from individuals, from corporations and from governments. A full list of all donors as of publication date is given on page 7 of this catalogue and I hope we have presented an exhibition that justifies their faith and support of this project.

I would like to mention a few of the many individuals who have contributed to this exhibition and catalogue. Mrs. Elsje Armstrong was not only a leading member of the funding group, but has played a vital role in obtaining the prerequisite financial support. Dr. Jack Blaney successfully chaired the exhibition committee, and we are deeply grateful for his outstanding leadership. Mr. Robb Watt, Director of the Centennial Museum, has led his staff successfully through the many labyrinths encountered in bringing together an exhibition of this magnitude. Mr Robin Inglis, our Secretary-General, has managed to keep the rest of our activities on schedule while at the same time giving *The Look of Music* the benefit of his leadership.

Others who have given of their time and wise counsel to bring about the success of the exhibition include Mrs. Pauline Hall, Mrs. May Kendrick, Mrs. Averil Kennedy, Mrs. Marigold Lyall, Mr. Gene Horvath, Mrs. Otto Koerner, and Baron Guilio Gatti-Kraus.

R. Michael Shields
President
Vancouver Museums and
Planetarium Association

FOREWORD
By the Director of Vancouver Centennial Museum

The citizens of Vancouver have been keen supporters of various forms of music since the earliest days of the city, although the community is young and some distance from the traditional centres of western culture. Until the development of *The Look of Music* exhibition, this interest was focused on musical performance, so much so that by the 1970's the city was home to Canada's leading symphony orchestra and had become renowned as a centre for the study and performance of early music.

With this exhibition, Vancouverites and visitors from around the world will have an unparalleled opportunity to gain an appreciation of the fascinating variety of instruments which have, since 1500, been the vital links between the creative genius of European composers and the virtuosity of countless musicians.

This is the most challenging and exciting single project yet undertaken in the 86 year history of the Vancouver Centennial Museum. An exhibition of this scale represents the working partnership of many individuals and institutions. The museological challenges encountered in planning and presenting this exhibition have been very great and I salute all the staff for meeting these challenges with energy, imagination and enthusiasm.

The Museum is deeply grateful to have had benefit of Phillip Young's scholarship and dedication to the exhibition. We are, as well, honoured to have received the support and involvement of so many of the leading North American and European museums whose cultural treasures are being featured in this unique exhibition. Our thanks go to all their directors and to the curators responsible for musical instrument collections.

Planning and financing this project have called for community involvement of a high order and the Museum has been fortunate to have received a greater measure of governmental, corporate and private support than for any other project in its history. Above all, our Trustees have repeatedly reaffirmed their support for the exhibition as the project has unfolded and new needs have arisen.

The Look of Music is a milestone in the cultural life of Vancouver and of Canada. We are proud to be the hosts and look forward to welcoming the thousands who will experience a very memorable event.

Robert D. Watt
Director
Vancouver Centennial Museum

the Look of Music

rare musical instruments
1500-1900

PHILLIP T. YOUNG

VANCOUVER MUSEUMS & PLANETARIUM ASSOCIATION
VANCOUVER

University of Washington Press, Seattle
Douglas & McIntyre, Vancouver

Published by Vancouver Museums and Planetarium
Association, 1100 Chestnut Street, Vancouver,
British Columbia
ISBN 0-919253-00-8 (cloth); 0-919253-01-6 (paper)

Distributed in Canada by Douglas & McIntyre,
Vancouver, British Columbia
ISBN 0-88894-290-7 (cloth); 0-88894-291-5 (paper)

Distributed in the United States by the University of
Washington Press, Seattle, Washington
ISBN 0-292-95784-0 (cloth); 0-292-95785-9 (paper)

Front cover: Seven-belled cornet reproduced by
            permission of Musée Instrumental, Brussels.

Design by: C. Holland
Typesetting by: Frebo Studio Limited
Colour separations, printing and binding in Canada by
Evergreen Press, Vancouver

Acknowledgements

The Author and Publishers would like to thank the following for permission to reproduce the illustrations in this book:

Private Collections, Vancouver for: 1, 26, 28, 36, 140, 141, 171, 202, 211, 218 Musée Instrumental, Conservatoire Royal de Musique, Brussels for: 2, 5, 7, 29, 60, 65, 70, 80, 91, 124, 126, 128, 129, 138, 156, 195, 207, 243, 246, 252, 253, 280, 292, 293, 296, 297, 301 Library of Congress, Washington, D.C. for: 3, 54, 63, 70, 220, 223 Museum für Hamburgische Geschichte, Hamburg for: 4, 11, 20, 62, 122, 145, 172, 174, 186, 192, 272, 283, 285 Collection of musical instruments of Dorothy and Robert Rosenbaum, Scarsdale for: 6, 42, 53, 64, 90, 104 152, 159, 161, 168, 184, 205, 206, 233, 236, 249, 262, 281 Musikinstrumenten Museum des Staatlichen Instituts für Musikforschung-Preussischer Kulturbesitz, Berlin for: 8, 9, 12, 17, 47, 58, 71, 105, 166, 268, 270, 278, 290 Musikinstrumenten Museum der Karl-Marx-Universität, Leipzig for: 10, 24, 25, 32, 33, 87, 88, 101, 212 Bate Collection, Oxford for: 69, 95, 169, 178, 180, 182, 183, 187, 194, 196, 197, 219, 221, 224, 230, 231, 232, 234, 235, 241, 242, 254, 255, 263, 288, 289 — on loan to Bate Collection from A.C. Baines: 13, 14 Musikmuseet, Stockholm for: 15, 43, 93, 98, 238, 245, 251, 256, 165 — on loan to Musikmuseet, Stockholm from Nordiska Museet Cliché Publimages, Musée Instrumental du Conservatoire de Paris for: 16, 21, 56, 57, 61, 77, 81, 92, 96, 99, 119, 133, 150, 175, 190, 265, 299 University of Victoria, Collection of Historical Musical Instruments for: 18, 170, 179, 193, 261, 286 Städt. Musik-instrumentensammlung, Munich for: 19, 103, 109, 225, 226, 227, 228, 229, 237, 244, 269, 279, 282 Germanisches Nationalmuseum, Nürnberg for: 22, 46, 51, 86, 116, 121, 147, 185 — Rück Collection in the Germanisches Nationalmuseum 110, 113, 114, 149, 163, 199, 201, 222, 250, 267 Musikhistorisk Museum og Carl Claudius' Samling, Copenhagen for: 23, 35, 83, 84, 107, 111, 130, 142, 144, 200, 204, 210, 259, 294 The Royal Ontario Museum, Toronto for: 27, 30, 38, 41, 117, 118, 123, 125, 127, 131, 135, 136, 139, 143, 146, 148, 155, 160, 216, 217, 260, 287, 291, 300 Museum of Fine Arts, Boston for: 31, 49, 108, 115, 120, 209, 213, 247, 275, 284 Yale University, Collection of Musical Instruments, New Haven for: 34, 37, 73, 132, 134, 137, 158, 177, 214, 273, 276 — on loan to Yale University from the Museum of Art, Rhode Island School of Design 157 The Metropolitan Museum of Art, New York for: 39, 40, 75, 82, 112, 153, 176, 215 Institute of Theatre, Music and Cinematography, Leningrad for: 44, 48, 50, 55, 59, 66, 67, 72, 78, 85, 94, 167, 173, 239 Bayerisches Nationalmuseum, Munich for: 45, 52, 68, 97, 100, 102, 106 Haags Gemeentemuseum, Holland for: 74, 76, 191, 248, 264 Victoria and Albert Museum, London for: 89, 271 Ward Music Ltd., Vancouver for: 151 The Montreal Museum of Fine Arts for: — Gift of the heirs of the estate of Mrs. Anna Loring 154 — Gift of Mrs. C.M. Drury 203 — Gift of the Hon. & Mme Joseph Edward Perrault 208 — Gift of Miss Y. Poisson in memory of her brother Jacques Gérard and her uncle Marc-Aurèle de Foy Suzor-Côté 302 Division of Musical Instruments, Smithsonian Institution, Washington, D.C. for: 164, 188, 198, 266, 274, 277, 295, 303, 304 Wilhelm Heckel KG. Biebrich for: 181, 240, 257, 258 Collection of Prof. & Mrs. Phillip T. Young, Victoria for: 189 Private Collection, Victoria for: 298 Heintzmann Ltd. for: 305

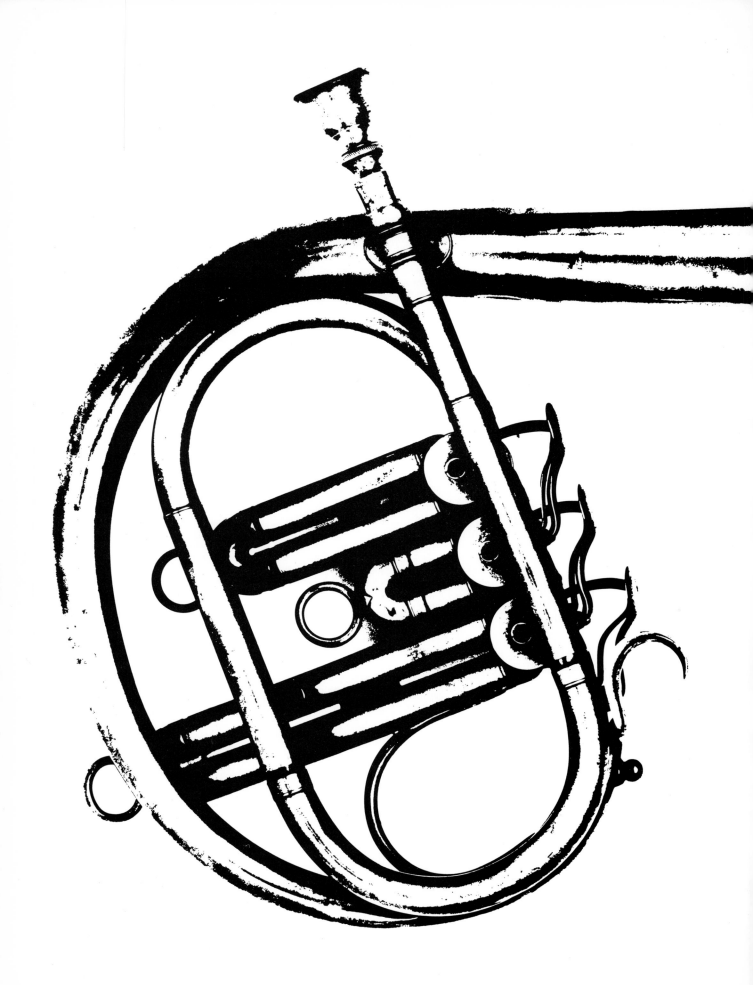

Contents

Introduction

Although there are many fine museum collections of historical musical instruments, there has never before been a public exhibition of this magnitude. Until recently there has been little general interest in early instruments, and even with the tremendous current growth of awareness, a few museums are unable to devote precious exhibition space even to the display of their own collections. Their treasures reside in basement or attic storerooms, visited only by staff and the occasional scholar. Moreover, for all our devotion to music of the past, we have until recently performed it only on modern instruments. We are so susceptible to the idea of human progress that we assumed today's instruments as well as today's playing techniques must be superior to those of the past.

In this century, however, a remarkable awakening has occurred. We have learned that music seldom sounds so well as when played on the instruments for which it was originally conceived. There are now many excellent recordings which illustrate this point: for example, the Beethoven Fourth Piano Concerto performed by Paul Badura-Skoda and the Collegium Aureum Orchestra; the great Mozart Bb Serenade by the Collegium Aureum winds; and the Bach cantatas by Vienna's glorious Concentus Musicus. Today, a growing proportion of the concert-going, record-buying public is willing to support first-rate performers who specialize in such "extinct" instruments as the natural (valveless) horn and the fretted clavichord. Happily, there now exists an informed public that will welcome the opportunity for further enlightenment which this exhibition provides. Beyond them are thousands more casual visitors to the Vancouver Centennial Museum who will come to this exhibition and thereafter hear music with a new awareness of the critical role of instruments past and present.

The Vancouver exhibition is unique in the history of organology, but there have been valuable precedents, particularly in England, where there has always been strong scholarly interest in historical musical instruments. In 1890 the Royal Military Exhibition in London produced a catalogue that is still included in most modern organological bibliographies; another famous exhibition was held at the Fishmongers' Hall of London. The Galpin Society, which acquired international importance soon after its founding in 1946, has mounted regular exhibitions throughout its thirty-five year history. The largest and most important, at the Edinburgh Festival in 1968, was drawn from museums and private collections within the United Kingdom. Most recently, London's Horniman Museum, the Victoria and Albert Museum, and the Musée Instrumental of the Paris Conservatoire have co-operated in preparing a travelling exhibition which has appeared at selected locations in England and France. Surprisingly few loan exhibitions have been held on the continent or in North America. What makes the Vancouver exhibition unprecedented, however, is that it brings together for the first time a selection of the most important instruments from two dozen of the world's principal collections. Many of the instruments have never before left their home museums; for the two-thirds that come from Europe, this is the first appearance in North America.

We are able to enjoy these instruments today only because some very knowledgable people were interested enough to search for them, and conscientious enough to provide the kind of care necessary to preserve them. Thanks to these people, we have originals on which to base modern copies. We also have the pleasure of viewing the instruments both in books and exhibitions and sometimes hearing them played. Some of the most famous collectors of past eras as well as many of the significant collections being formed today are represented in the Vancouver exhibition. These include for example, Alexander Kraus, Wilhelm Heyer, F.J. Fetis, Victor Charles Mahillon, Cesar Snoeck, Daniel Scheurleer, Carl Claudius, Dayton C. Miller, Ulrich Rück, Paul de Wit, Belle Skinner, Canon Francis Galpin, R.S. Williams, Crosby Brown, Philip Bate and Robert Rosenbaum.

The task of planning and organizing this exhibition has been the "opportunity of a lifetime". The choice of specimens has been the sole responsibility of the writer, and, of course, no-one will be entirely satisfied with the final selection. It may help, however, to know that the choice was determined in part by factors other than my own preference. For example, only a few lenders agreed to loan everything that was first requested. Five major museums declined to participate and many other important collections could not be approached because of budgetary limits. Here and there an instrument has been included partly because its owner requested that it be exhibited, while offering other more important and unique specimens as well. We were forced to decline generous offers from many private collectors because the inclusion of more lenders would have been too complex and expensive. The exhibition includes a few probable forgeries, though they are usually identified as such, but museums firmly recommended against other dubious examples which I would have included on grounds of general interest. Also a great many choice instruments are regularly used in performances and could not be spared for a lengthy exhibition such as this; two examples are Yale's Andreas Ruckers harpsichord (1640) and the Metropolitan Museum's restored Antonio Stradivari violin (1691). Unfortunately, a strict condition of all loans prevents anyone from playing a single note on any of the instruments in the exhibition. However, during the exhibition the Museum itself and other Vancouver musical institutions will offer numerous concerts and recitals using instruments similar to those on display.

The exhibition is "wind heavy" only because museums are more willing to loan winds than the more fragile strings and keyboards. We also decided to limit this exhibition to western European instruments made between 1500 and 1900 and to exclude, for the most part, purely folk and amateur types. We further decided that the well-established organological and socio-cultural importance of the musical instruments used by the first British Columbians deserves independent and definitive treatment in a separate exhibition.

The labels "Classical", "Romantic", and so forth, are intended simply as a guide based on familiar signposts. In a few cases where these categories conflict with the instrument's actual date of manufacture, our intention was to indicate the historical period in which most specimens of the same type would normally be found. Examples are Nos. 18 and 109.

Finally, this publication is intended primarily to answer basic questions and to arouse the interest of musicians and the general public. However, I hope there will be useful things in it for the scholar as well.

Mounting this exhibition was a huge undertaking that has occupied many people over a period of five years. I am personally grateful to all those who have helped, particularly the staff of the Centennial Museum. They are genuinely creative professionals, association with whom has been especially rewarding to me. Carol Mayer, Curator of Decorative and Applied Arts, has been Curator in charge of the exhibition, and I doubt that anyone other than myself knows how much credit she deserves. I will always be grateful to her. Dr. John Henry van der Meer has again and again put his awesome knowledge at my disposal with patience and wit. I am grateful to my colleagues Dr. Gordana Lazarevich and Dr. Erich Schwandt for reading portions of the text. My wife has been sounding board, translator, shirt-folder, and an endless source of encouragement and good humour.

Phillip T. Young

School of Music,
University of Victoria.

Prologue

People have always made musical instruments. Even before they learned to howl or sing, human beings *seem* to have clapped hands, stamped their feet, and slapped their chest, thighs, or buttocks. Very soon came the hollow log and both gourd and strung rattles. Much later, but while still in a state we would call primitive, humans learned to make end-blown and cross-blown flutes, single and double reeds, lip-vibrated animal horns, and plucked strings.

Primitive societies did not use "musical" instruments primarily for enjoyment or artistic expression, but rather as effective equipment for magical and ritual ceremonies to enhance or preserve the well-being of the participants. These rites quickly changed to social events once fears were relieved, and primitive people must also have appreciated the skill of virtuoso instrumentalists as well as the pleasure of group music-making much as we do today.

There are very few surviving examples of the early European instruments in use before the beginning of the period covered by this exhibition. One exception is the beautiful Scandinavian *lur*. Because this instrument was usually made of durable bronze, a few specimens remain from well before the time of Christ. The *lur,* a gracefully curving horn with the bell held aloft, was traditionally used in pairs by its warrior-players.

Like the Greek and Roman horns and trumpets, the *lur* seems to have served mainly as a means of sounding battle signals. Except for these metal horns, most early European instruments — what we would call strings, keyboards, percussion, or winds — were made of natural, organic materials that eventually disintegrated. Consequently, Frederick Crane's[1] recent book which lists all known medieval musical instruments contains only 564 entries, including such simple musical devices as whistles, scrapers, and rattles.

Students are always surprised to learn how much our western European musical instruments owe to the older cultures of Asia and the Near East. Among the more important European types directly traceable to Asian instruments are the lute, guitar, cittern, psaltery, dulcimer, harp, rebec, violin and nearly all other bowed strings, as well as various drums, cymbals, trumpets, and oboes. It is interesting to speculate how different European music would be today had a great wall or a broad ocean separated Europe from the Near East soon after the first future Europeans migrated westwards.

By 1500, the principal types of European instruments were well-defined. From the beginning of the 16th century on, these basic types were continually improved and refined as a result of conscious experimentation.

1. Frederick Crane, *Extant Medieval Instruments* (Iowa City, 1972).

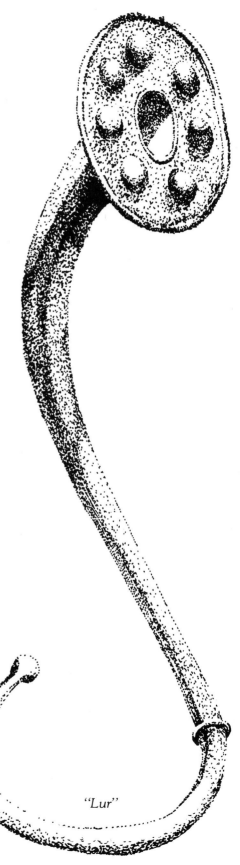

"Lur"

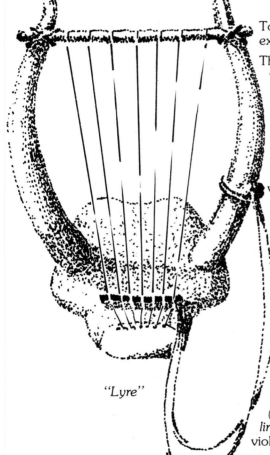

"Lyre"

To trace some typical lines of development leading to the instruments in this exhibition, we must, however, start not in Europe but in Asia.

The lyre is believed to have originated in Mesopotamia. The original lyre was a sound-box made of a large tortoise shell to which two horns or arms of wood were affixed. These were joined at their further ends by a crosspiece or "yoke", and strings were stretched between yoke and sound-box. These provided a number of pitches exactly equal to the number of strings. The lyre eventually spread to other cultures and became the best known instrument of classical Greece, where it developed into two co-existing forms, the amateur's lyre (described above) and the professional musician's *kithara,* a more complex, sophisticated version. (A stylized form of these Greek lyres is used so frequently as a symbol of music that it has become a cliche.) Sometime in the Middle Ages the lyre acquired a central fingerboard behind its several strings, which permitted rapid stopping of each string and therefore much more intricate musical roles. The result was an instrument very much like the later Welsh *crwth* in our exhibition (No. 29). Very soon the two arms and the yoke were removed, leaving adjustable pegs in a pegdisc or pegbox, a neck lying under the strings and a soundbox made in a variety of shapes. This was, in fact, a rudimentary guitar, ukelele, or cittern. It also resembled that most beloved instrument of the Renaissance, the lute. The lute, however, came to Europe by quite a different route, via the Arab *al'ud.* We now think that the bow was discovered about 900 A.D. in Central Asia and that it was quickly adopted for use with all sorts of previously plucked string instruments. The bow's first European appearance was in Spain, where it was used with what was even then becoming the national instrument, the guitar. The bowed guitar *(vihuela d'arco)* is regarded as a predecessor of the Renaissance *fidel* and *lira da braccio* (No. 33). These were both immediate forerunners of the violin and its chief competitor, the viol.

The very first keyboard instrument was the organ, an invention that dates from around 250 B.C. and was originally known as an "hydraulus". The name led many authorities to believe, until recently, that its pipes were made to emit sound by water rushing through them, but now we know — in part thanks to the discovery in 1931 of a few pieces of an hydraulus in the ruins of a Roman town near Budapest — that the water served only as a means to keep the air pressure steady, as in the modern galvonometer, and that in all important respects the hydraulus was a true organ with rudimentary keyboard, a windchest, and a single rank of pipes. Speaking of its use in Roman times, Cecil Clutton has written: "The hydraulus was used at public entertainments, such as those connected with lions and Christians, and it is therefore understandable that the early Christians found no liturgical use for an instrument about which they had somewhat sensitive recollections."[1].

1. Anthony Baines, editor, *Musical Instruments Through The Ages* (Second edition, Penguin, 1966).

Within several centuries, however, these prejudices had been put aside, and the organ was adopted by the Christian church, in whose service it was to achieve its most important use. Eventually, well before 1500, the organ existed in three principal forms: the *portative,* carried by a shoulder sling in processions, its bellows pumped with one hand while its keyboard was played by the other; the *positive,* self-contained in a large cupboard-sized box of ideal size for a small church or castle gallery; and in a third variety which was much larger, as enormous in overall size if not in richness of tonal resources as anything built since. Later on, near the beginning of the sixth century, the keyboard was fitted to instruments other than the organ. Certainly by 1500, the keyboard had been coupled with a mechanical plucking device to produce the early harpsichord (and its smaller, simpler versions, the spinet and the virginal) and with a tapping device to produce the clavichord. Two more centuries elapsed before the keyboard was coupled with the dulcimer to produce the earliest piano. The important point here is that the various keyboard strings were *new* in 1500. This exhibition includes several of the earliest keyboard instruments still in existence. (Nos. 1, 37, 40, and 41 for example).

Several basic types of wind instruments have been used since the earliest times; yet wind instruments remained relatively unchanged, or at least without refinement, until the Renaissance. Winds have always been considered poor cousins to strings and keyboards, probably because they are less difficult to construct and are made in greater number. To this day, the development of wind instruments has not been so carefully traced as the development of strings and keyboards and is therefore not so well understood. In World War II, it is hard to avoid the conclusion that bombs took a proportionately greater toll of wind instruments than either strings or keyboards because the latter were more carefully protected. The basic wind shapes offer less possibility of artful ornamentation than keyboards and strings. Perhaps this too accounts in part for their relative neglect by historians.

Drums and other percussion devices were some of the earliest musical instruments, though later on they showed the least development. A peak in their use occurred in the Middle Ages, very likely because they provided much needed "colour" and because of the agonizing slowness with which strings and winds were developing. Much medieval music characteristically employs a simple drum beat, tambourine, castanets or clappers, finger cymbals, and/or sets of tuned bells, either to colour the random ensemble of various strings and winds, or in support of voices, or in purely instrumental dance pieces. Following its important role in medieval music, percussion steps well into the wings until very much later when it reappears first as a single timpanist in Haydn and Mozart's orchestra. Beginning in the 19th century percussion developed slowly into the orchestra percussion section and the modern percussion ensemble, while maintaining a traditional role in military and ceremonial music.

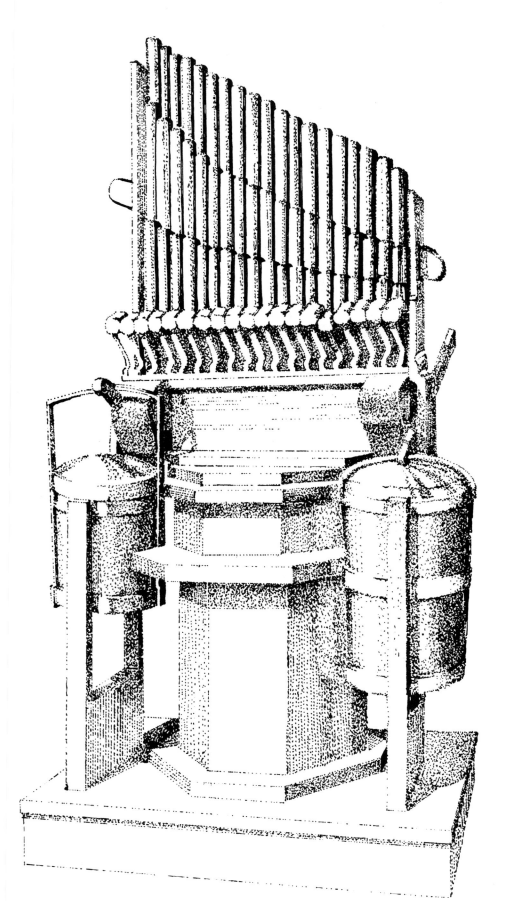

Hydraulus

The following colour reproductions have been brought forward to the beginning of the book as representatives of some of the highlights of the exhibition and of the historical and artistic development of western musical instruments.

1. SPINETTA

Dominicus Pisaurensis

Dated 1534

The honour of "No. 1" has been assigned to this Italian *spinetta* because it is possibly the oldest instrument in the exhibition and because it is from the collection of a Vancouver family. At one time it was part of the celebrated Kraus Collection in Florence, which is known to have also included two harpsichords by this well-known maker. This is the first time the instrument has been exhibited in modern times. This *spinetta* is a compact, simple harpsichord with one string per pitch. As is characteristic of Italian *spinette*, it is made mainly of cypress, in this instance has four sides of uneven length, and is shown in its black-painted outer case (made much later), from which it would be removed and placed on a table for performances.

Dominicus Pisaurensis was born in Pesaro, but spent most of his life in Venice. Surviving instruments bear dates from 1533 to 1600, a suspiciously long working period for one individual, which has led to the suggestion that there may be two makers of this name.

L 174.0 cm.; D 57.0 cm.; H 91.3 cm. Compass E-f' Private collection, Vancouver.

7. SET OF SIX CRUMHORNS

Anonymous, French

Late 16th century

There are other presumed sets of crumhorns, but none in a contemporary fitted case that seems to have been designed both to protect the instruments physically and to preserve their integrity as a set made to be used in consort. A random assortment of Renaissance or 17th century winds do not usually work well together unless designed by a single maker for that purpose. The typical one-piece form does not permit adjustments in tuning to match other instruments, so the matched-pitch set is almost a necessity. Beyond that, tone quality varies from maker to maker and model to model, unless the instruments are executed as a set. This applies to all winds of this era and is the reason for even later sets such as Nos. 61 and 68.

The crumhorn is a marvellous instrument, even if used too frequently in early music groups today. A double reed is located in an enclosed wind cap (chamber) and is activated by blowing through a slit near it in the top. The player's lips therefore have no direct control of the reed and of either pitch or dynamic (volume) level. The tone has a pronounced buzz, gorgeous by itself and especially effective in unison with recorders.

All six of these instruments are stamped just above finger hole 1 with three devices similar to those that appear on Nos. 3 and 4. The bass (largest) crumhorn has two brass sliders along its curved portion that permit the player to choose which of two possible bass notes will be produced when the keys themselves are both closed.

Boxwood with brass.

No. 610, soprano H 40.0 cm.	Doubled finger hole 7, one side plugged with wax
No. 611, alto H 57.9 cm.	
No. 612, alto H 58.3 cm.	One tuning hole (not fingered) below finger hole 7
No. 613, alto H 59.5 cm.	
No. 614, tenor H 81.5	1 swallowtail key under protective brass box
No. 615, bass H 96.0 cm.	2 swallowtail keys, one above the other, under protective brass box

Musée Instrumental, Brussels, 610-615.

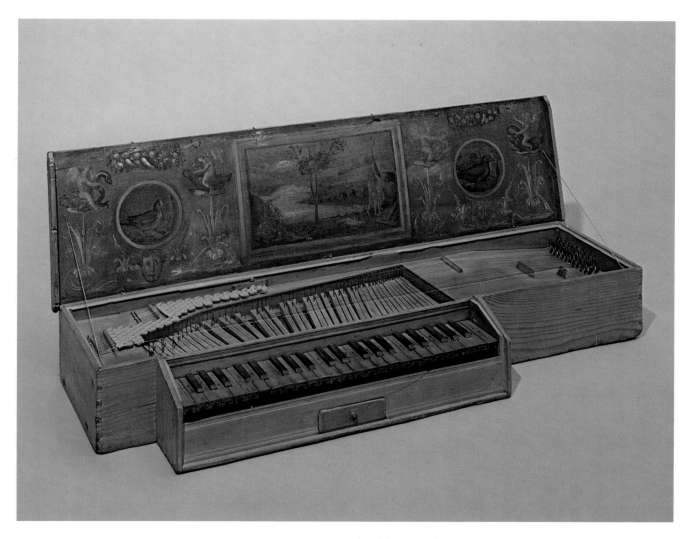

40. CLAVICHORD

Onesto Tosi, Genoa

Dated 1568

This is thought to be one of the two oldest, playable clavichords in existence. It is a fretted clavichord (the only kind until the late 17th century) which means that each string furnishes several different pitches, depending on where along its length the string is actually struck. The striking is the most important feature of the instrument. Clavichords employ a brass tangent on the inner end of each key, and this tangent strikes the appropriate string when a key is depressed. Thus the clavichord is somewhat similar to the later piano, striking its strings rather than plucking them, as the harpsichord, virginal and spinet do.

As old as it is, this instrument stays in tune remarkably well and rarely needs retuning!

Many celebrated musicians of former times considered the clavichord far superior in expressiveness to any of the plucking keyboards, but because of its small size and the nature of its simple striking mechanism, it produces only a very low volume level. Its sound is too small and soft to be audible except in a family living room.

This Tosi clavichord can be heard on a wonderful recording made by Bernard Brauchli, performing Renaissance pieces appropriate to the instrument. The disc is produced by Titanic (no. Ti-27).

Compass C-c'''. L 119.0 cm., H (on stand) 98.4 cm., D 42.5 cm. Museum of Fine Arts, Boston, 17.1796.

41. HARPSICHORD

Giovanni Celestini, Venice (fl 1583-1610)

Dated 1596

This beautiful instrument may be the finest that has found its way to Canada. There may be other instruments of similar quality and interest in private collections, but if so they have been kept a secret. This is a typical example of one sort of 16th century Italian harpsichord; small, one manual, with two sets of eight-foot strings, separate inner and outer cases, the inner of cypress and cedar. In all probability the outer case is later; its inside lid painting is judged by the Royal Ontario Museum to be early 17th century. The boxwood natural keys have arcaded fronts with a trefoil under each arch, and the accidental keys are stained black. The rose is of wood and parchment.

Actual inscription on name board: *Joannes Celestini Veneti MDXCVI*

Compass four and a half octaves: C-f'' with short octave. H 179.7 cm.
Royal Ontario Museum, Toronto, 913.4.97

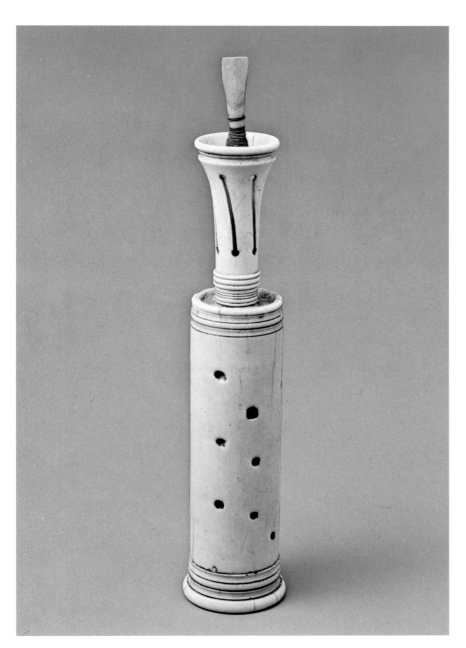

10. RACKETT

Anonymous, Tyrol

Late 16th century

Racketts have an ingenious design that compresses a long air column into a short block of ivory or wood, creating a low-pitched instrument with dimensions more appropriate for a soprano. Just how this works can be seen in the close-up of No. 105. The Renaissance rackett is otherwise quite different from the Baroque model. Its double reed projects from the location of the bell on No. 105, and its lowest tone is emitted from a hole at its base rather than from such a bell. The double reed combined with cylindrical bore causes it to behave acoustically as a stopped pipe, and therefore to sound an octave lower than would otherwise be true. The Renaissance model does not overblow. Its 10 to 12 fingerholes are obliquely bored and covered not just by finger tips but in some instances by other portions of the finger.

This beautiful ivory specimen is thought to be the earliest in existence. There may in fact be only two other Renaissance examples that survive, both of ivory and both in Vienna.

Body H 18.0 cm., pirouette and reed H 9.5 cm.; overall H 27.5 cm. Musikinstrumenten-Museum der Karl-Marx-Universität, Leipzig, 1414.

22. BASS TROMBONE

Isaac Ehe, Nürmberg (1586-1632)

Dated 1612

To quote Anthony Baines once again, this is simply "the most beautiful trombone in existence".

One will recognize the flat, hinged stays and long conical bell of trombones discussed on page 43. The extra two turns and connecting tubing at the top contribute to the overall lower pitch as on the modern bass trombone, but in addition, a supplementary slide extension is added there, manipulated by the left hand via the long rod with the knob that one can see in the photograph. A further rod and knob swivel from the stay of the main slide to permit one to reach a distant sixth position. Seventh position was not yet in use.

The maker's name on the bell is in such a decorated script that until very recently it was believed to be "Johann Isaac Ehe" and that name was duly listed in a number of books. The correct name is given here.

Full bell inscription: MACHT ICH ISAC EHE NVRMB 1612

Brass. L 149.0 cm., overall tube length without mouthpiece 422.5 cm., bell dia. 12.4 cm. Germanisches Nationalmuseum, Nürnberg, MI 168.

19. NATURAL TRUMPET

Hanns Hainlein, Nürnberg
(1596-1671)

Dated 1632

The Hainleins are one of the great Nürnberg families of master brass instrument makers that dominated their craft to the same extent and for precisely the same two centuries as the great violin maker families of Cremona. Hanns was a generation after Sebastian, the founder of the dynasty, and might logically have been a second son after Sebastian II (junior? 1594-1655), but this has not yet been firmly established. Notice, the relatively slight degree of bell flare, compared with trumpets of only 50 or 100 years later; for example, Nos. 112 and 114.

Full bell inscription: MACHT HANNS HAINLEIN MDCXXXII. An emblem separates "Hanns" and "Hainlein", a cock or hen's head (a pun on "Hahn" and "Hain"?) with the maker's initials on either side.

Brass. L 81.5 cm., bell dia. 9.5 cm. Stadt. Musikinstrumentensammlung, Munich, 67/95

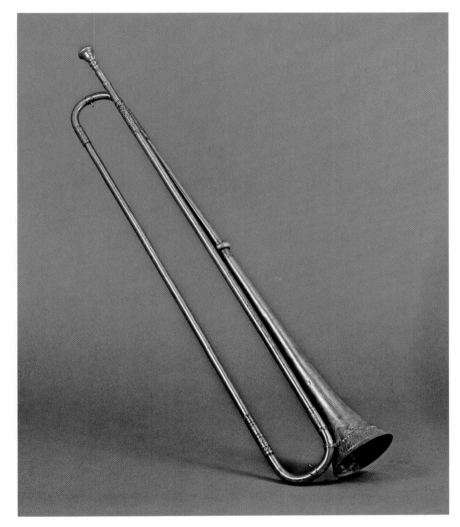

58. FLUTE IN C

Hotteterre

circa 1700

Nos. 58 and 59 have to be among the most beautiful flutes in existence. They *look* Baroque with their prominent turnings, heavier than those on any later flutes to the present day, very much akin to the magnificent turnings on the Denner bassoons (Nos. 47 and 48) and almost all oboes to 1800. The Bressan flute (No. 70) is similar in this way.

All four existing Hotteterre flutes have the stamp with name, no initial, and the anchor trademark. It is reasonable to hope that the identity of that Hotteterre who so stamped his instruments will become known to us in the next few years.

Boxwood, with ivory mounts (the foot is entirely of ivory). One silver key, *not* brass as reported elsewhere. In three sections. L 70.5 cm. Musikinstrumenten-Museum des Staatlichen Institut f. Musikforschung-Preussischer Kulturbesitz, Berlin, 2670.

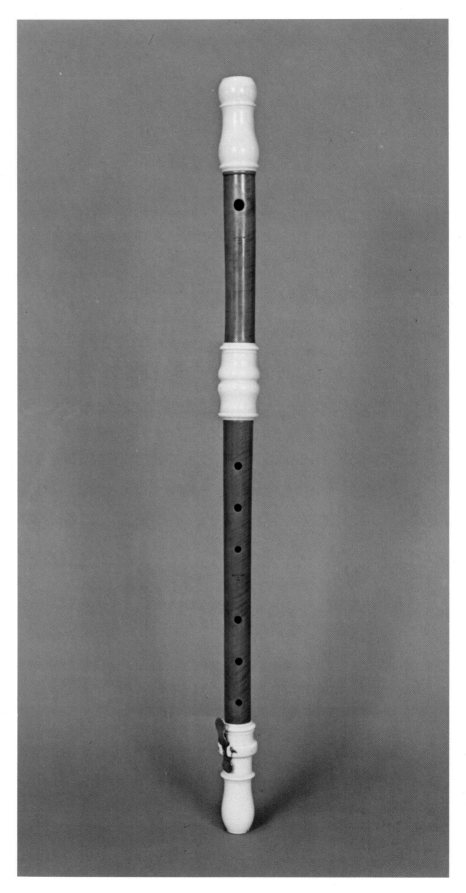

122. LUTE

*Joachim Tielke, Hamburg
(1641-1719)*

Dated 1691

This lute was later converted to a guitar, and certain parts were altered or replaced. What remains from the original is the body, comprised of 11 rosewood ribs outlined with narrow strips of ivory inlay, and the neck, cut down to much narrower width but with some of the inlay on the back surviving. The belly (the flat top of the body) and the pegbox are not original. Much as we wish the instrument had been left in its original state, the conversion shows that it must have had a notably good tone to begin with and that it was recognized as too special to be discarded outright. Other lutes fared worse. Label: JOACHIM TIELKE / *in Hamburg* / *An. 1691.* This lute is No. 57 in G. Hellwig's book on J. Tielke, listed in the bibliography.

Body L 52.0 cm., body W 31.0 cm., body depth ca. 15 cm., neck L 28.0 cm. Museum für Hamburgische Geschichte, Hamburg 1953.65.

97. CHALUMEAU

Stuehnwal

We know neither first name, town, country, or dates of this maker, and this is his sole known instrument. Its importance lies in the fact that there is nothing else like it preserved anywhere. We believe this to be the simple 17th century folk *chalumeau* that Johann Christoph Denner "improved", but it has the two keys (including a speaker) which have been assumed to be the principal ways in which Denner improved it. In other words, is this one by Stuehnwal an earlier anticipation of Denner, or a copy of Denner, or was this the usual *chalumeau* of the late 17th century, which Denner then "improved" by elongating it in proportion to its bore and perhaps in other ways? The initial cause of this confusion was an enigmatic statement by J.G. Doppelmayr in 1730, but a number of others soon further complicated the question and today it seems hopeless to try to resolve it.

Boxwood, unmounted, with two brass keys on diametrically opposed holes. Bore, upper end 1.2 cm. lower end 1.5 cm. H 29.0 cm. Bayerisches Nationalmuseum, Munich, Mu 137.

100. CLARINET IN G

Johann Wolfgang Kenigsperger, Roding (?) (- 1752)

On this instrument the third key is finally in place, giving the low e and b' that were not previously available, but the key is on the back, operated by the thumb of the lower hand. It is not known whom to credit with the addition of the third key or later additions. J.W. Kenigsperger is also represented in *The Look of Music* by Nos. 93 and 103.

Plumwood, with horn mount between main joint and bell. Three sections. Three brass keys. In G. H 51.8 cm. Bore 1.1 cm. Bayerisches Nationalmuseum, Munich, Mu 110.

52. CHALUMEAU

Johann Christoph Denner, Nürnberg (1655-1707)

It was Denner who invented the clarinet, and this is the only one in existence today bearing his stamp. It must be the rarest, most valuable woodwind in existence.

The term *chalumeau* has been widely adopted lately to distinguish this earliest form of clarinet, which has only a recorder-like foot joint rather than a flared bell. No. 79 by Johann Christoph's son Jakob is a true clarinet, in that terminology. I will admit to disliking this distinction, and would prefer that the term *chalumeau* be reserved for the simple cylindrical, single reed, folk-type instrument that existed before Denner and which he is said to have improved. The important thing is to recognize four types; the simple instrument without speaker key just mentioned, the improved version with speaker key (No. 97, see comment there), a considerably lengthened *chalumeau* with speaker key (Nos. 52 and 98) and therefore increased capability over either of the preceding, and finally, a similar, lengthened *chalumeau* ending in a flared bell (Nos. 79, 99, 100).

"Speaker key" denotes the clarinet's octave key, but since the clarinet overblows at the interval of a 12th rather than at the octave as the oboe and saxophone do, a different term than "octave key" is needed, hence "speaker key". The two keys on this instrument are the speaker on the back above the thumb hole and the a' key on the front, exactly as on the modern instrument.

Three other Johann Christoph instruments in this form were in the Germanisches Nationalmuseum, Nürnberg, but were lost in World War II. Even so, fortunately and appropriately, that museum has the largest collection in existence today of instruments by this native son, as well as a great many by other native sons.

Boxwood, unmounted, with two brass keys covering diametrically opposed holes. H 50.0 cm. Bore 1.3 cm. at lower end of mouthpiece-barrel, but 1.43-1.45 cm. in main section. Bayerisches Nationalmuseum, Munich, Mu 136.

133. VIOLIN

Antonio Stradivari, Cremona (1644-1737)

Dated 1724

This instrument belonged to Pablo Sarasate (1844-1908), the great Spanish virtuoso. He was accepted as a student at the Paris Conservatoire when 12 years old, and it is there in the Musée Instrumental du Conservatoire that this violin normally resides today. The instrument was actually presented to him as a boy by Queen Isabella of Spain, and he used it throughout his career. A successful copy of it was made for him by Vuillaume (Nos. 296 and 297) and was sometimes used by Sarasate at rehearsals.

Of this particular instrument, the Brothers Hill in their standard book on Antonio Stradivari have this to say: "There still remain to us some fine examples of 1721 and the following years, which, if not comparable with those of the preceding decade as regards beauty of wood and varnish, are in no way inferior to them in point of form and construction; indeed, some of the finest-toned instruments date from these years. The violin invariably played upon in public by Senor Sarasate is of the year 1724. Though unattractive in appearance, it captivates all hearers by its tone."

Body L 35.7 cm. Body widths 17 cm., 11.5 cm., 20.5 cm. Musée Instrumental du Conservatoire de Paris, E.1729.

158. HARPSICHORD

Johann Adolph Hass, Hamburg (...1740-1776?)

Dated 1770

This gigantic harpsichord was found in Vienna in 1892 by the prominent collector Morris Steinert, from whom it was acquired eventually by Miss Belle Skinner, owner of a collection now at Yale University. For some time its inscription was believed to give the date 1710, suggesting an earlier founder of the Hass family than Hieronymous (No.156), but it is generally accepted today to read "1770", and the instrument is now assigned to Hieronymous's son, very much admired then and now in his own right.

There are two manuals and one 16' stop, two 8', one 4', and one 2'. The upper manual slides inward to engage its 8' stop. The handstops to control the choirs are found on the wrestplank. The case itself has a double bent-side and its exterior is painted to resemble tortoise-shell. The inside of the lid and the inside of the case are decorated with chinoiserie in gold over a red lacquer background. The keyboard area (keywell) is faced with laburnum wood panels.

The instrument represents the most advanced, complex stage of development the harpsichord had reached just before it was driven off the concert platform by the new fortepiano.

Overall L 277.5 cm. Overall W 100.0 cm. Compass FF-f'''. No.1 of this maker in Boalch, 2nd edition. Yale University, Collection of Musical Instruments, New Haven, 251.

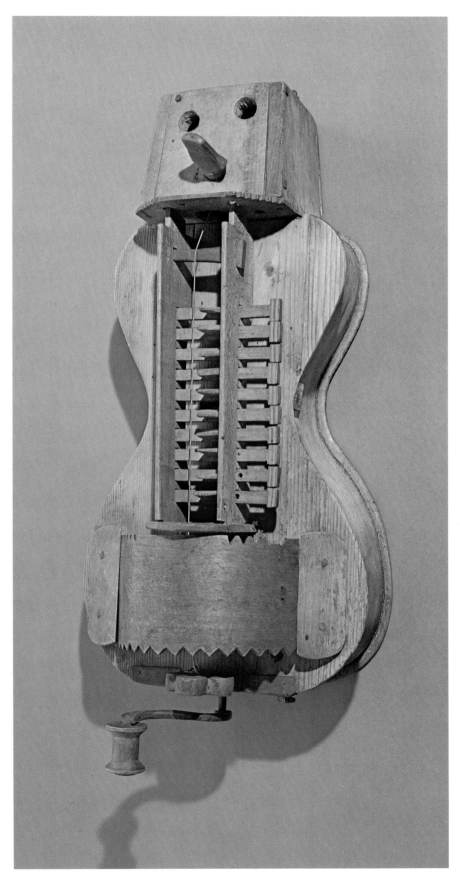

120. HURDY GURDY

Anonymous, Quebec or Northern Maine

18th century

This hurdy gurdy was acquired just a few years ago by the Boston Museum and may be the only instrument in *The Look of Music* that was actually made in Canada other than the Heintzmann piano. Easterners will recognize immediately the characteristic white pine of which so much early furniture was made in the first settlements and in rural areas for long after that. It has just three strings - only one *chanterelle* and two drones - and the rib on one side of the body is missing, affording a rare look at the interior of a hurdy gurdy.

Overall L 57.8 cm. W 26.7 cm. overall H 16.5 cm. Museum of Fine Arts, Boston, 1977.9.

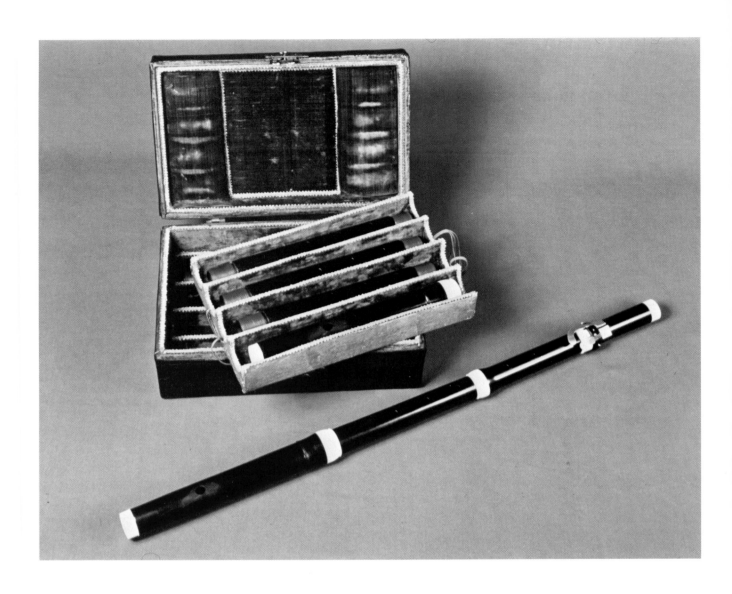

71. FLUTE

Johann Joachim Quantz, Berlin or Potsdam (1697-1773)

Frederick the Great (1712-1786) acquired flutes with nearly the same enthusiasm, it would appear, as Dayton Miller (see No. 70). None is more beautiful or more treasured than this gorgeous specimen made expressly for Frederick by his flute teacher and court musical director. It also bears the extra, second key that Quantz himself invented. This key produces a true d#', in which those with very acute musical hearing detect a slight difference from eb', produced by the normal single key found on flutes of this time. Quantz is also credited with inventing the head joint tuning slide (not a feature of this present instrument), but we have noted that this actually may have been first accomplished by Jacopo Neni in the Renaissance, whose

claim to that important advance has been recognized only in the last 20 years when a bass flute (No. 6) with a similar feature was first reported.

Quantz himself was the first great flute virtuoso, travelling to all parts of Europe and to London, playing with and for Handel, Scarlatti, Hasse, and nearly all the other major musicians of the day. His book, *Essay of an Instruction How to Play the Transverse Flute,* is an important source of our knowledge of performance practice during that era.

Ebony, with ivory mounts and two silver keys. L 67.4 cm. with longest of five upper joints. There are two head joints, the difference in length of which is .05 cm. The alternate upper joints differ in length by precisely .7 cm. and are distinguishable from each other by one to five notches in the edges of their upper tenons. In black case lined with green velvet, with tray (which has no space for an alternate lower and/or foot joint; if it had, this would have to be described as two separate flutes, as in the example of No. 67). Musikinstrumenten Museum des Staatlichen Instituts f. Musikforschung-Preussischer Kulturbesitz, Berlin, 5076.

280. MULTI-BELL CORNET

Adolphe Sax, Paris (1814-1894)

circa 1852

Despite the amusing absurdity of its appearance, this instrument represents a serious attempt to solve an old problem. Philip Bate says this cornet and its comparable trombone model are ''among the most remarkable instruments ever to appear''. The trombone slide is very nearly perfect as a means of altering pitch, better than a valve will ever be. Any valve adds or subtracts a fixed length of tube which is, at best, ideal for one or perhaps a few notes, but not for all those which result from using it in combination with other valves. In this invention by Sax, every change in pitch is produced through its own valve (never used in combination with another) and through its own tube ending in its own bell. Every pitch therefore has its own perfect length of tube, whereas conventional valve instruments must rely on compromises that come close. Unfortunately, even for a cornet, it weighs too much and is too cumbersome — but it works.

H. 56.3 cm. Musée Instrumental, Brussels, 2467.

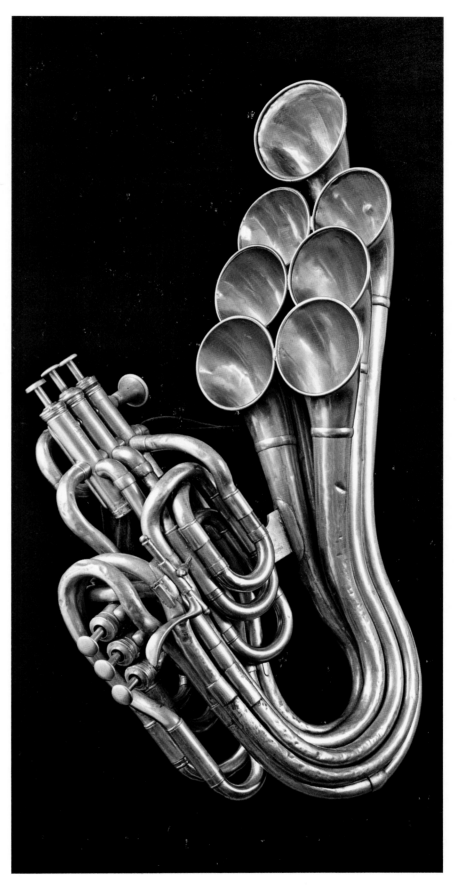

281. MULTI-VALVE TROMBONE

Adolphe Sax, Paris (1814-1894)

circa 1852

Sax's serial numbers are a fiendish code that no mere human mind has yet been able to crack. Even so, it is interesting (and surely coincidental) that only five digits separate the serial numbers of No. 280 and the present No. 281. Sax made at least several of the multi-bell instruments (with widely differing serial numbers), both cornets and trombones. When it had become obvious that

their weight was simply too great, he concentrated on this one-bell, multi-valve model as an alternative, and it enjoyed considerable success. This trombone version is apparently used in the Brussels opera house to this day. Recalling the compact "theatre-model" bass clarinet (No. 249), it is easy to imagine how well this form of trombone is suited to use in a cramped opera-house pit, where it is always a challenge to find room to use the standard slide. The advantages of a six-valve instrument are explained under No. 280.

Overall H. 66.0 cm. Collection of Musical Instruments of Dorothy and Robert Rosenbaum, Scarsdale, 217.

The Renaissance—1450 1600

The word "Renaissance" recalls so much that is significant in the history of civilization: Michelangelo, Josquin, the printing press, the Medici, Gesualdo and Marenzio, Botticelli, the discovery of America, Dürer, Brueghel, Titian. Although we rightly venerate the remarkable achievements of the Renaissance, we no longer look upon that period as a radical rebirth of creativity. We are growing continually more aware of significant achievements during the preceding "dark ages". The Renaissance neither broke with the immediate past centuries nor had any cause to repudiate their direction. The path to Dufay was well established by de Vitry, Machaut, Landini, Dunstable, and the others.

With instruments, too, there was steady and significant evolution during the Middle Ages. Improvements in the dependability and flexibility of the keyboard, for example, and of both bowed and plucked strings, set the stage for the harpsichord and clavichord, as well as the organ, and for liras, the viols, and violins. Perhaps there was less remarkable progress with winds, and especially woodwinds. Until the 15th century these seem to have been restricted to crude shawms, flutes and recorders, the gemshorn, bagpipes, bladderpipes, and very limited trumpets. There followed, however, a mushrooming of types and sophistication as the fifteenth gave way to the sixteenth century, and there began to be *families* of flutes, recorders, crumhorns, rauschpfeifen, shawms, dulcians, trombones, and cornetti. Such families of various pitches and sizes are a characteristic of Renaissance instrumentation, and extended as well to bowed strings, though less so to plucked. There is no need here to debate which came first, an idiomatic instrumental music which then spawned such a wealth of instrumental colour, or more expressive and stable-pitched instruments which then unleashed the imagination of composers. The point is that *both* occurred and that music of the late Renaissance therefore has a very special appeal to those who love musical instruments.

How were instruments used in this splendorous era? Then and for some time to come the church was most important. Though its power and its influence were perhaps showing the first cracks, the church was still the major force in musical development. I have long held the secret conviction that Giovanni Gabrieli represents the apogee of Renaissance music, both sacred and secular. As musical director of Saint Mark's Cathedral in Venice, he deployed choirs of voices and instruments on opposing balconies in distant parts of his church and so created an ideal medium for his opulent, brilliant music. His achievement was not matched until the cantatas of Bach received definitive performance in the Thomaskirche a century and a half later. We think that Gabrieli's *Sonata pian'e forte* (1597) may be the first composition ever to include specific, contrasting dynamic indications and the first as well to specify what instruments were to be used on each of its contrapuntal lines. Until Gabrieli, such critical decisions were simply left to the director-leader, who might change the arrangement arbitrarily from one performance to the next.

The other major force in musical patronage during the Renaissance was the nobility, with its magnificent courts and palaces. No member of the nobility had a more dazzling musical retinue than Maximilian the Great (1459-1519), Emperor of Germany, who further secured a place in the history of western musical instruments by commissioning a long series of woodcuts which recorded for posterity his lifestyle and pleasures. These woodcuts show a number of his musicians and a great many of their instruments; they also record some of the more common combinations in which the instruments presumably were used. Few other iconographic sources from the period contain so much helpful information. The series of woodcuts takes the form of a long procession of equestrian groups and ornate wagons, reminiscent of a circus parade, in which most of the instruments then in use may be seen. There are a few folk instruments as well as those employed by the court professionals. The interested reader will be able to find scenes from the *Triumph of Maximilian* reproduced in many recent books about musical instruments. (Jeremy Montagu's *The World of Medieval and Renaissance Musical Instruments* is an excellent source which is listed in the bibliography at the end of this book.) Beyond triumphal processions, instruments found regular use in the court chapel, in palace entertainments, and sometimes as suitable objects of study by the nobility themselves. Today, we are amused by the fact that most strings, in particular the lute, were considered genteel and therefore suitable for the nobility to play, whereas winds were consigned to the less wellborn.

Beginning in the 16th century we find the earliest instances of a maker's "stamp" (usually initials, name, and/or trademark, burned into the wood) or a label pasted inside the soundbox. This seems to be a sign of growing self-respect on the part of skilled instrument makers and to indicate the point at which they began to think that their identity was of interest to others. The cylindrical flute by Claude Rafi of Lyon (No.5) is one of the earliest surviving instruments which bears its maker's name. We are only now beginning to uncover the identity of some of the makers who used only initials (No. 12) or some kind of hallmark (Nos. 2, 3, 4, 7, 9. and 11, for example.) In this area of research, progress is indeed slow.

The Renaissance section is a special strength of this exhibition. Each specimen is unique, like no other in existence and of course, irreplaceable. Yet this awesome reality should not obsure the more important fact that ordinary people built these instruments with love and with great skill and sensitivity and then used them to make music as beautiful as any ever written.

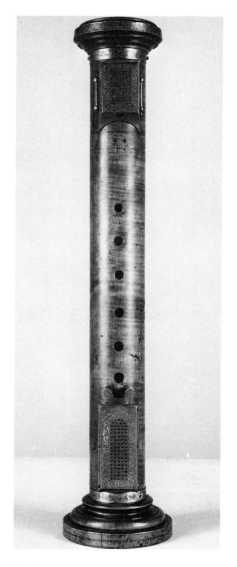

3. TENOR RECORDER

Anonymous, German

circa 1580

This is a fine example of a typical Renaissance recorder – clean lines, one-piece construction, graceful flare at the lower end. The (lowest) seventh-finger hole is doubled, analogous to the twin touch of a swallowtail key (see explanation, No. 2), and the player used wax to plug whichever little-finger hole wouldn't be needed. It has no maker's name but has the following marks for which we have yet to establish a maker's identity. The lip or sharp edge on which the air stream divides is found on the back side of this instrument rather than on the front, which is most unusual. This particular specimen is no stranger to major exhibitions of instruments. It was displayed at the Royal Military Exhibition, London, in 1890; at the Crystal Palace Exhibition, London, in 1900; and at the Music Loan Exhibition, London, in 1904.

Reddish brown wood, unmounted. In C. H 63.0 cm. Library of Congress, Washington, D.C., 1240.

2. COLUMNAR ALTO RECORDER

Hans Rauch von Schratt (. . .1535. . .)

Only three recorders exist in this unusual design, all presumably from the Renaissance and all three possibly made by Hans Rauch, one of the earliest woodwind makers to mark (some of) his instruments with his name. He also used a trademark of two trefoils with stems curving to the right (here, just above the upper finger hole).

This recorder is blown through a slot at the top, while its lip is covered otherwise by a hinged, perforated brass grill, as is the single key. The key has a swallowtail or fishtail touch, that is with projections to both the right and left to permit either right or left little finger to reach that key, as one preferred. At that early time and for two centuries to come, it was not customary as it is today that with all woodwinds, the player's *right* hand is assigned to the holes and keys furthest from the mouth.

Maple with brass mounts. H 51.0 cm. Musée Instrumental, Brussels, 189.

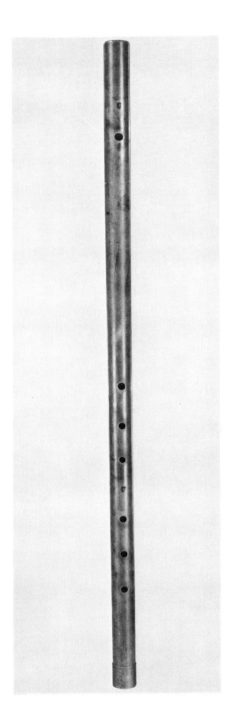

5. TENOR TRANSVERSE FLUTE

Claude Rafi, Lyon

(1515-1553)

This maker is of special interest because more is known of him at this time (even so, not much) than any other 16th century woodwind maker. Research is helped appreciably by the fact that he appears to be one of the earliest to stamp his name on his instruments, usually with a crest that encloses a griffin (?). Only in the last year or so has it been established that a "G.Rafi" and an "M.Rafi" were also flute makers and assumedly of the same family. Claude seems to have enjoyed a wide celebrity, even to the extent of having his praises sung by poets, including Marot and Ronsard.

Three flutes – then termed alto, tenor, and bass – were in use in the 16th century, all with cylindrical bore, that feature to be eventually replaced with conical bore by the Hotteterres in the 17th century and then restored by Boehm in the 19th. Like other Renaissance woodwinds, transverse (held out to the side) flutes are made in a single section with virtually no surface ornamentation. One can find the stamp "C.RAFI" and the griffin crest just above the mouthhole and the crest alone between finger holes 3 & 4.

Boxwood or maple. L 71.7 cm. Bore 1.8 cm. Outside D. 2.85 cm. at mouthhole, 2.6 cm. at finger hole 6. Musée Instrumental, Brussels, 1066.

4. BASS RECORDER

Anonymous, German

circa 1550

Straight, unadorned lines, one-piece construction, and an inversely conical bore - all characteristic of Renaissance woodwinds - are seen here. The brass swallowtail key is protected by a perforated wooden sleeve or "fontanelle". This instrument is stamped with a single device not unlike the two on No. 3. The hole through which one blows is on the edge of the top surface. The various brass bands are both reinforcement and decoration. The small knob at the top is purely decorative.

Maple (?) with brass mounts H 85.9 cm. Museum für Hamburgische Geschichte, Hamburg. 1924.206.

6. BASS TRANSVERSE FLUTE

IA (Jacopo) NENI

circa 1600

Nothing whatever is known of this maker, although the simple fact that his name is stamped on this single specimen gives him special interest. We know the names of very few woodwind makers of this period. The flute is cylindrical but with the slightest reduction along its length, internally and externally. Because it is longer than an alto or tenor, it is made in two sections. The head-joint tenon is of exceptional interest because it is inscribed with nine concentric calibrations as a guide in tuning; that refinement was not possible, of course, with a one-piece instrument. This may, then, be the earliest example of a tuning slide. There were originally nine raised, external rings around the socket of the main joint, but four were reduced to accommodate a brass band added later as a repair of a crack. Neni's stamp and a shield containing a six-point star are found above the mouthhole and the shield alone between finger holes 3 and 4.

Boxwood, with brass repair as noted. Detailed measurements are given by Eric Halfpenny, former owner, in the Galpin Society *Journal*, Vol. XIII (1960). In G. L. 91.0 cm. Bore 2.62 cm. at upper end and 2.47 cm. at lower end. Collection of musical instruments of Dorothy and Robert Rosenbaum, Scarsdale, New York, 14.

8. ALTO POMMER

anonymous, German

17th Century

Four instruments (Nos. 8,9,12 and 17) have been loaned by the Musikinstrumenten-Museum in Berlin from their extraordinary set of instruments that until the late 19th century were the property of St. Wenzel's Church in Naumburg, now in East Germany. Not only is this Naumburg group a unique collection of instruments used in an actual church as a participant in its services, but its acquisition and augmentation are documented in careful inventories kept by the church and preserved today with the instruments in West Berlin. This instrument is next to smallest in a set of eight pommers now in the Musik-instrumenten-Museum, six from Naumburg and two other, remarkably similar ones from the old Marienkirche in Danzig. The smallest is 55.2 cm. high and the largest 271.5 cm. tall.

Pommers, also known as shawms, employ a double reed which is not confined to a windcap but taken directly into the mouth; they have a much less raucous, strident quality, we believe today, than was reported by their critics in the Renaissance. The soprano and altos are the direct predecessors of the oboe. This specimen has a single brass swallowtail key under a fontanelle. Its fragile bell rim is protected by a decorative brass band. As was customary in the Renaissance and for more than a century later, the key pad is simply a piece of cloth or soft leather, sewn in place on the key through perforations in the key flap.

Boxwood with brass. Lowest tone: a. H 74.7 cm. Musikinstrumenten-Museum des Staatlichen Instituts f. Musikforschung-Preussicher Kulturbesitz, Berlin, 646.

9. TENOR POMMER

Anonymous, German

Early 17th century

This is another Naumburg instrument and a member of the Berlin group of eight pommers (see preceding instrument, No. 8). On this as well as the two larger members of the set, a metal crook projects to put the reed in a more comfortable position for the player. Two swallowtail keys, one above the other, are on the upper surface for the little finger of the lower hand, while two thumb keys for the same hand are on the back. All four keys are protected by the long fontanelle. At the top by the crook socket is stamped a single trefoil, its stem to the left, while on the flat surface at the very end of the bell is stamped ''CR''.

Maple with brass keys and mounts. The crook is a replacement. Lowest tone: d. H 134.9 cm. Musikinstrumenten-Museum des Staatlichen Instituts f. Musikforschung-Preussicher Kulturbesitz, Berlin, 644.

11. BASS DULCIAN

Anonymous, German

16th century

Like the rackett, the dulcian is made of a single block of wood but has only two parallel tubes, jointed at the bottom. It has a conical bore throughout that begins with a double reed on a short metal crook into the narrower side of the twin bore, then turns and rises in the other bore to a short, separate bell. The dulcian or curtal is the predecessor of the bassoon and differs from it only in number of keys and construction, the bassoon being made in four separate, wood sections plus crook vs. the dulcian's single block. The bass dulcian is termed *Choristfagott* in German because of the practice of making it in the same pitch as choir organs for use in churches.

This particular dulcian has worn finger holes and many scars. It must have had long use and been a very good instrument. The brass swallowtail key has an unusual touch that suggests a Viking helmet, while the key on the back side is very plain. Both are covered by protective, perforated brass boxes. The lower narrower brass band at the top is a crude later repair; the brass cup over the lower end is also later.

Maple with brass. Overall H 103.9 cm., bell dia. 10.9 cm., bell H.15.4 cm. Museum für Hamburgische Geschichte, Hamburg, 1928.389.

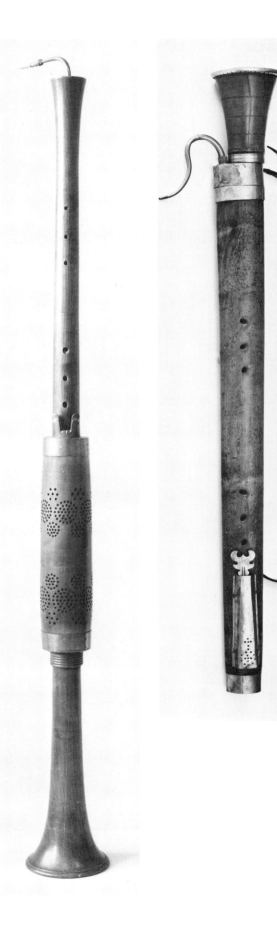

12. TENOR DULCIAN

Anonymous, German

Early 17th Century

Another of the Naumburg instruments, this tenor is made from a block of tiger maple, considered by some to be the most beautiful of all wood. It shows much less wear than the previous specimen, perhaps because it was owned by a church and was surely not used as regularly as the more common bass. This dulcian is *gedakt,* or covered; a muffled, softer tone was accomplished by placing a perforated cap over the bell opening. The English have a gift for choosing apt terms and have designated this a "pepper shaker" bell for obvious reasons. During the Renaissance, entire families of dulcians from soprano to great bass (*Quart-* and *Quintfagott*) were made, in keeping with the taste for consorts of single types of instrument.

Like the tenor pommer from Naumburg (No. 9) this instrument is stamped with a single trefoil with stem curving to the left and the initials (?) "CR". It has two brass keys covered with brass boxes, one key with a swallowtail touch.

Overall H 69.6 cm. Total L. of air column approx. 144.0 cm. Musikinstrumenten-Museum des Staatlichen Instituts f. Musikforschung-Preussicher Kulturbesitz, Berlin, 650.

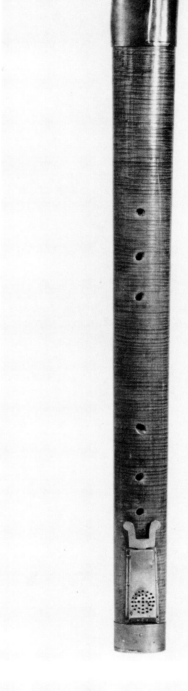

13. CORNETTINO

Anonymous, German

Dated 1518

Perhaps the only true hybrid instrument of such distinction, the cornett family combines the cup mouthpiece of brasses with the woodwind finger-hole method of changing pitch. It was again and again proclaimed by discerning observers of the time to be the most perfect of all winds and perhaps of all instruments, especially in support of the human voice. Its most important period was between 1550 and 1650, in the course of which it figured prominently, for example, in the antiphonal choirs of Giovanni Gabrieli and in Monteverdi's orchestra for his opera *Orfeo*. Much later it was used by Bach in 11 of his cantatas, and it remained a fixture of German small-town bands even into the 19th century. Then, sadly, its flame died out and its technique was lost forever, perhaps only fifty years before the beginning of the rebirth of interest in early music performed on original instruments.

The *cornettino* is the smallest size of which we know, with a range from d' to e" or f"'. This particular instrument was formerly in the collection of Canon Francis W. Galpin, the eminent English organologist in whose honour the Galpin Society is named. The interesting construction of *cornetti* is described briefly under No. 14. The middle silver mount is engraved with the date "1518" and the lower mount with (the initials?) "III K" between two arrows. The mouthpiece is not original.

Plum (?) covered with black leather and with silver mounts. L 41.5 cm. Bate Collection, Oxford, X501.

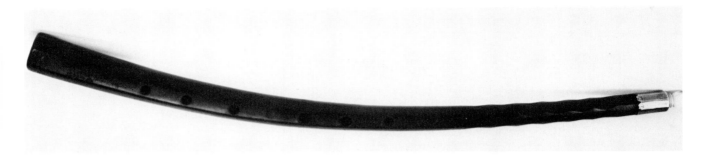

14. CORNETT

Anonymous

circa 1600

This is the standard cornett, as are Nos. 15 and 16, with a range roughly the same as violins of that day, g to a'', sometimes extended upward on the cornett by a gifted player but not by more than a few notes.

Curved cornetts, as opposed to straight (see No. 17), cannot be turned on a lathe or given their conical bore by straight drilling, so from their first appearance their bores have been carved in mirror image into the opposing surfaces of two pieces of wood, then the excess wood removed to form the exterior of the two halves. At this point, the duplicate halves are glued together and bound with black leather for further strengthening and air-tightness, after which the finger holes are drilled. Traditionally the exterior is finished in octagonal cross-section and an intricate diamond pattern cut into its upper end.

The importance and principal period of the cornett were discussed under No. 13, while other aspects will be set forth under Nos. 15, 16, and 17. The present instrument, like No. 13, was at one time in the collection of Canon Galpin.

Wood covered with black leather, two silver mounts. L 58.4 cm. Bate Collection, Oxford, X500.

15. CORNETT

Anonymous

17th century (?)

Cornetts are descended from simple instruments made from animal horns and tusks. The most important is the oliphant, a military or ceremonial signal horn most often made from an elephant tusk and usually carved in elaborate design. It is not surprising that cornetts were also made from ivory, although apparently always with the traditional octagonal exterior rather than any relief carving. Since a leather covering would defeat the purpose of using ivory, such *cornetti* are made in two halves and merely glued to a tight bond.

Few *cornetti* retain their original mouthpieces. A mouthpiece, if present, is most likely a later replacement. This example lacks any clue whatever to maker, date or country of origin.

L. 56.7 cm. along outside of curve. Musik Museet, Stockholm, 173.

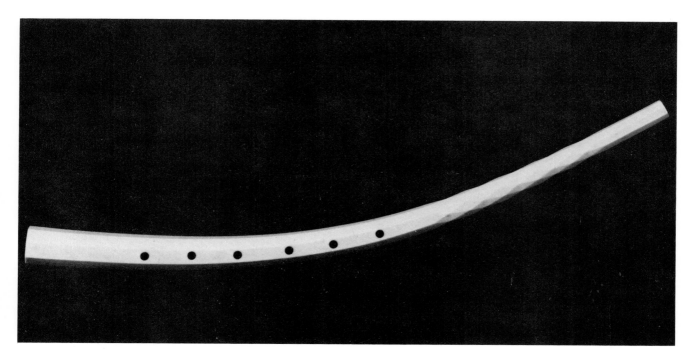

16. CORNETT

Anonymous

End of 17th century?

This instrument is striking for its slim lines and lack of metal mounts of any sort. Its seams are invisible even under magnification. The traditional diamond facets along the upper portion are especially handsome, too. The instrument was found in Italy and presented to the Musée Instrumental in the 19th century.

The designation "cornet" first occurs in English as early as the 15th century, but recently the modified "cornett" spelling has been widely adopted to distinguish the Renaissance instrument from the obsolete brass band instrument of the 19th and early 20th centuries. The Italian terms *cornetto* and (two or more) *cornetti* are also in general use, as is the German *Zink* and (two or more) *Zinken*.

L 57.8 cm. along outside of curve. Musée Instrumental, Paris, E.138, C. 630.

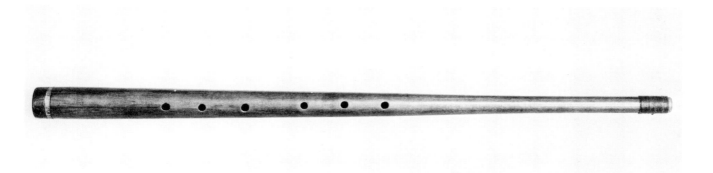

17. MUTE CORNETT

Anonymous, German

circa 1670

Curved *cornetti* are much more common, but the straight "mute cornett" until the 18th century coexisted with the curved. More important than the bore contour, however, is the fact that straight cornetts were turned on a lathe and bored and were given an integral mouthpiece carved into the narrower end. The result of the smaller, integral mouthpiece is a softer tone. Wind players would also describe it as offering less resistance. The size of the mouthpiece cup is much smaller than any brass mouthpiece in use today or any other example included in this exhibition.

This instrument is another from the Musikinstrumenten-Museum in Berlin, and originally came from St. Wenzel's Church in Naumburg. The brass band is a later repair.

Maple. Lowest tone: a. L 65.0 cm. Musikinstrumenten-Museum des Staatlichen Instituts f. Musikforschung-Preissicher Kulturbesitz, Berlin, 661.

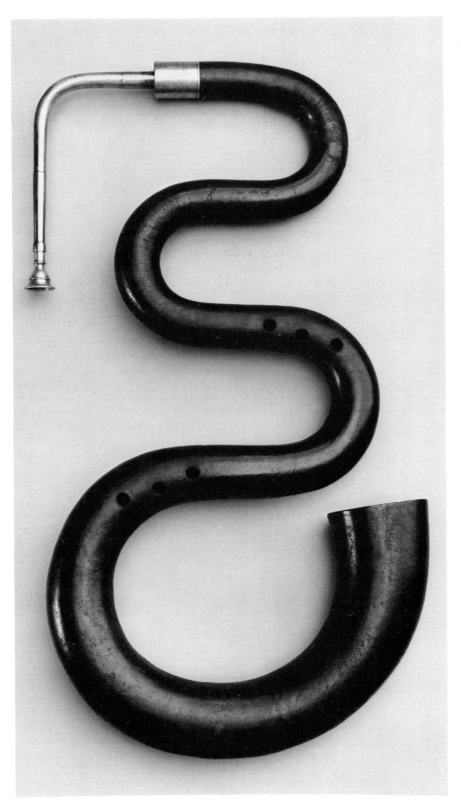

18. SERPENT

Anonymous, French?

Early 19th century

Although this specimen dates from the end of the period in which the serpent played its important role, it is virtually indistinguishable from the earliest examples. This is a bass cornett by traditional definition, but Sibyl Marcuse has rightly suggested that it would be more accurate instead to consider it allied to the cornetts and serving as their bass. The bore of a serpent must be extremely wide in proportion to its 2.10-meter length, in order to bring its fingerholes into playable reach. The usual placement of its six finger holes (with a long gap between two sets of three) makes no acoustical sense at all, but it works. Like the cornett, the serpent is always made in two vertical halves, then glued and bound tightly with leather. An ivory or bone mouthpiece is usual. This brass one is not original.

H 83.2 cm.; W 43.5 cm. School of Music, University of Victoria, 1970-2

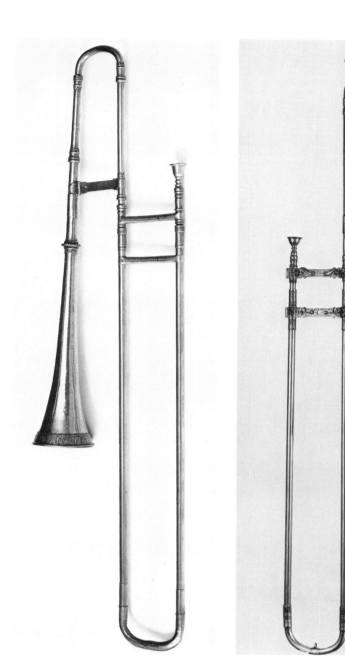

21. TENOR TROMBONE

Georg Ehe, Nürnberg (1595-1668)

Dated 1619

The Ehe family, like the Hainleins (No. 19), were a major brass dynasty in Nürnberg. This would seem to be the only surviving instrument by this member of the family. As Anthony Baines has pointed out, it retains the bore of a tenor but has a tube length that may be enough longer than a tenor to have made it a *secund* or *terz* trombone (pitched a major second or third below standard pitch). The mouthpiece is not original.

The slide stays of this instrument are of the flat, hinged variety, made with a certain degree of flexibility or "give" in order to withstand stress. A band of leather circles the tubing at point of contact with stay, and half of the stay's mounting clamp is hinged to enable it to swing open on its hinge to encircle the tube and its leather buffer. When the clamp closes, a small hook and eye hold it shut, gripping the tubing firmly without complete rigidity. This intricate connection may indicate that either soldered joints were not always reliable at this time, or that such play between the inner and outer slide helped it to move more freely.

Full bell inscription: MACTICH GEORG EHE NURMBR/MDCXIX

Brass. L. 130.0 cm., bell dia. 12.5 cm. Musée Instrumental du Conservatoire de Paris, E.754, C.660.

20. TENOR TROMBONE

Cunrat Linczer, Nürnberg (...1568-1609)

Dated 1587

There are only a few trombones in existence older than this, and those only by a few years. It can be clearly seen how little the trombone has changed in 400 years since this one was made. Apart from the long cone-shaped bell vs. the more flared modern design, the most conspicuous difference is the lack of a water key in the Renaissance.

The instrument is entirely of brass with richly engraved stays or braces between the main sections of tubing. There are also two renderings of the Nürnberg arms. This trombone was found at the beginning of the 19th century under the floor of St. Gertrude's Chapel, Hamburg.

Full bell inscription: CUNRAT 9 LINCZER ME FECIT NURM 1587

Brass. L. 124.0 cm., bell dia. 12.0 cm. Museum für Hamburgische Geschichte, Hamburg, 1928.328.

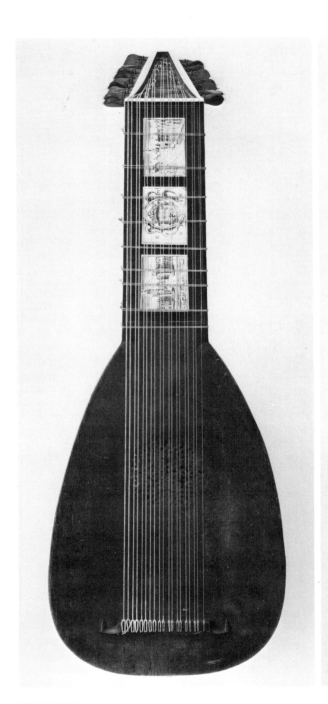

23. LUTE

Christofolo Cocho (. . .1640-1654. . .)

Circa 1640

This beautiful ivory lute is the work of an important maker in whom there is much interest and about whom there is much uncertainty. He worked in Venice and used a gold eagle as a sign outside his shop, according to labels found in several instruments. It seems likely that he was English (one or more labels identify him as ''Christopher Cocks''), but he Italianized this to ''Christofolo Choc'' as well as to the version found in this Copenhagen lute.

This lute has nine double courses and one single. There are three inlaid panels in the fingerboard, the outer two of Venice and the middle one with a design around which are four letters C M V R, the order in which they are read not at all certain.

Actual label: *CHRISTOFOLO COCHO AL AQUILA D'ORO IN VENETIA,* with a second, later label indicating that the instrument was repaired in 1712 by Johann Christian Hoffmann, Leipzig.

L 83.5 cm. body L 48.5 cm., body W 30.0 cm. Musikhistorisk Museum og Carl Claudius' Samling, Copenhagen, 96a.

44

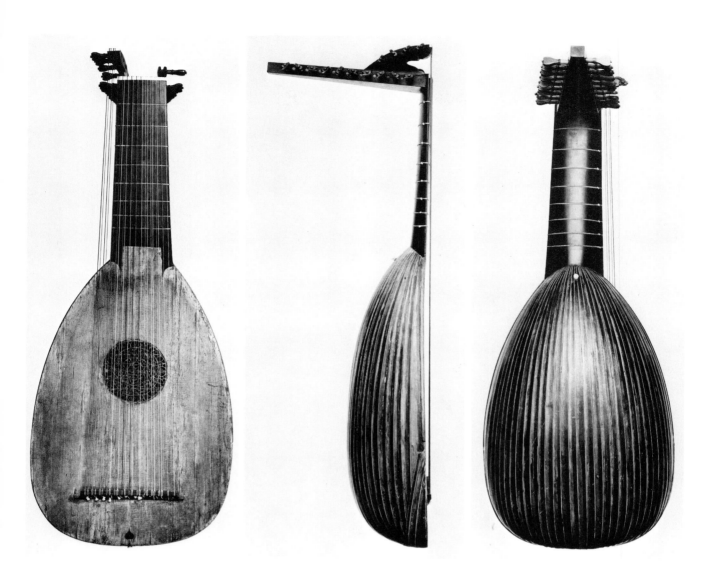

24. LUTE

Wendelin Tieffenbrucker, Padua (. . .1572-1611. . .)

Dated 1551

The contradiction in the dates above is as yet unexplained. The date on the label inside this lute has been established for some decades, while the most authoritative treatment to date of the Tieffenbruckers, that in the monumental dictionary *Musik in Geschichte und Gegenwart,* must err in listing only one Wendelin in a long succession of 15 or more instrument makers of this name and presumably of the same family. The most important of these are Wendelin, Kaspar or Gaspar, and three named Magnus. Tieffenbruck is the small town in Bavaria from which the family

came originally. As with many other notable German lute-makers of the 16th century, Laux Maler and Hans Frei, for example, a number of the Tieffenbruckers immigrated to Italy and even Italianized their names, "Duiffoprugcar" being a well-known example (however un-Italian it may sound).

This plain but elegant lute has nine double courses and four single, a later type of stringing than was used in 1551. Lutes are always fretted with tied-on gut strands. The first time one picks up a lute it is always a shock, so unbelievably light and delicate are they for their size. It has often been said that a fine lute literally trembles in response to the touch.

L 92.0 cm., body L 55.0 cm., body W 35.0 cm. Musikinstrumenten-Museum der Karl-Marx-Universität, Leipzig, 492.

25. CHITARRONE

*Magnus Tieffenbrucker, Venice
(...1580-1621...)*

Circa 1600

A brief account of the Tieffenbrucker family is given under No. 24. This instrument is probably by Magnus II (dates above).

Very recent research by Douglas Alton Smith suggests that this long-necked lute was invented in 1588 or 1589 in Florence by one Antonio Naldi, who then commissioned Magnus II to make one for him. This Leipzig treasure is not likely the first specimen, but must be one of the first.

Basically, the *chitarrone* is not a bass lute, meaning one with all its strings tuned well below the usual lute, but instead it is a lute designed particularly for accompanying and so has a number of bass strings lying alongside the usual upper courses. A bass note can then be used alternately with contrasting notes on the upper strings, for example. Note the very delicate triple rose (sound hole) and the flawless shell (back) made of 33 separate maple ribs.

Six double courses and eight single. L 188.8 cm., body L 62.0 cm., body W 34.7 cm. Musik-instrumenten-Museum der Karl-Marx-Universität, Leipzig, 512.

26. CHITARRONE

Alexandro Marcellino, Padua

Dated 1612

This is a most curious instrument about which there is some difference of opinion. The upper neck, from the point where it narrows appreciably, is very crudely made, especially the main peg box, which normally would be open rather than having a back to it. The upper pegbox and the scroll are not a bit more contorted and strange-looking than many others of established pedigree. Only recently did I spot the nicely aged label inside which reads as given below. Marcellino is not listed in any of the standard directories of luthiers, but that is not necessarily conclusive. The body itself appears old and seems very large. There were 11 strings to the main pegbox and six to the upper.

Label: ALEXANDRO MARCELLINO
fecit anno 1612
ni Padova

Overall L 158.0 cm., body L 64.0 cm., body W 41.8 cm. Private Collection, Vancouver.

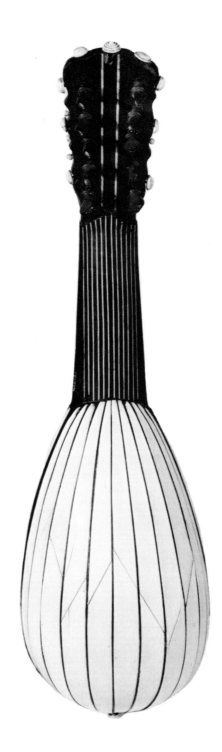

27. MANDORA (?)

Petrus Bulocta

Dated 1584

It seems likely that this was originally a small treble lute, later converted into a kind of mandolin. The pegbox is a much later type than would be found with strings tied to a bridge. At the same time, the body, neck, and fingerboard are quite handsome. It is now strung with five double courses and lacks the tied-on frets which it undoubtedly had in both its original and converted states. This maker is not listed in the standard directories, and his dates and place of work are therefore not known.

L 54.6 cm. Royal Ontario Museum, Toronto, 908.13.1

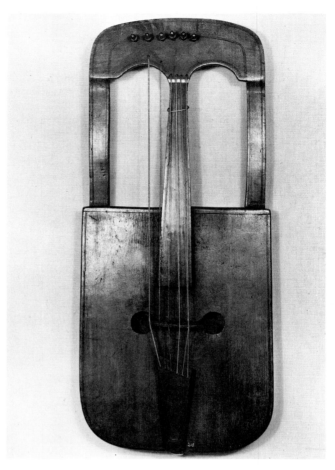

28. DULCIMER

Anonymous, Italian

17th century (?)

The psaltery is a plucked zither that is first seen in medieval painting and then found continuously to the present day, often a folk or home instrument plucked with the fingers or often a feather or other plectrum. The harpsichord is considered a psaltery coupled to a keyboard plucking mechanism. The dulcimer is very similar, but its strings are tapped with soft hammers, and in that sense it is a forerunner of the piano. Although there are no mallets that accompany this specimen from a Vancouver collection, it is believed to be a dulcimer because of its movable bridges, the placement of which has a role in providing two pitches per string. The instrument is stored in a much later, outer case lined with brocade.

H 9 cm., W 70 cm., D 30.5 cm. Private Collection, Vancouver

29. CRWTH

Anonymous, Welsh?

18th century (?)

In any number of ways, this is one of the most fascinating instruments in this exhibition. Its evolution and importance were mentioned briefly in the Prologue, for it is a major link between the Greek lyre and bowed and plucked medieval instruments. Until 1949, when a circa 12th century version was unearthed at Danzig, no known examples existed of an earlier date than this presumed 18th century specimen (apparently unchanged since the Middle Ages) and a few others of similar age.

Traditionally made from a single slab of wood except for its separate belly, the body includes arms and a yoke from which are tied six gut strings, four bowed and able to be fingered against the central neck, and two lying off the neck to the side and plucked. The usual bridge is very similar to the *tromba marina's* (Nos. 30 and 31), one foot resting on the belly and the other continuing through a hole to transfer vibrations to the back, as with a sound post.

H 55.9 cm., W 23.5 cm. Musée Instrumental, Brussels, 218.

30. TROMBA MARINA

Anonymous, German

17th century

This odd instrument has existed from medieval times and is played today as a folk instrument as well as in performances of early music. One bows its long single string *above* the point that one lightly fingers (touches) the string, producing a metallic harmonic. The other peculiarity is its bridge, one foot of which projects through a hole in the belly and presses against the back, behaving as a sound post on a violin. The other bridge foot very lightly touches the belly, against which it vibrates producing a distinct buzz.

There are two implausible theories as to its use and the source of its names. One suggests that it is a "marine trumpet" because sailors used it on deck as a warning signal to other ships at night. The other explains its German name "Nun's fiddle" must derive from the trumpet-like sound that made it an acceptable substitute for unladylike brass in a convent orchestra.

H 189.25 cm. Royal Ontario Museum, Toronto, 908.13.7.

31. TROMBA MARINA

Anonymous, Italian

Late 17th century

The remarkable thing about this example is its unusual number (fifty) of sympathetic strings inside the sound box. Sympathetic strings are not bowed or plucked directly but vibrate audibly, in sympathy with other strings tuned to the same pitch which *are* bowed or plucked. The best-known example is the 18th century *viola d'amore* (Nos. 147 and 148) which has gut bowed strings that activate wire sympathetic strings, producing a lovely ethereal sound. The *baryton* (No. 210) is another instrument with sympathetic strings.

This specimen was found early in this century in an old farmhouse in Cheshire, England, where it had been for many years before being acquired by Canon Francis Galpin.

An unusually complete description of the instrument and its playing technique is to be found in the book "Ancient European Musical Instruments", by Nicholas Bessaraboff, Cambridge, 1941. H 192.0 cm, W 25.0 cm., D 37.5 cm. Museum of Fine Arts, Boston, 17.1733.

32. LIRA DA GAMBA

Antonius Brensius, Bologna

Dated 1592

Quite apart from other characteristics, several important Renaissance bowed strings carry the designation *da gamba*, which means played on the leg, or *da braccio*, which means played on the shoulder. The *lira da gamba* is a larger, bass version of the *lira da braccio* (No. 33), sharing many features therefore but not all, and held in a different position. These are among the most important 16th century bowed strings, contributing substantially to the development of even the *violas da gamba* (viols) but especially of the violin. The *liras* lasted not much more than 150 years, and were replaced in the 17th century by the *viola da braccio,* in effect the violin family.

The chief characteristics of the *lira da gamba* are its large body, well-defined centre bouts, a wide fretted fingerboard with two off-board drone strings and 9-14 fingered melody strings, a flat peg disc in heart or leaf-shape rather than a peg box, either frontal or rear pegs, and a wide flat bridge to facilitate chordal playing. The present example is also notable for the ridges, more decorative than structural, that lead from the centre of the belly out to the corners. The peg disc is particularly handsome, but regrettably it is a reconstruction, as are the tailpiece, fingerboard and neck. Unfortunately, this is the only instrument of Antonius Brensius that survives.

H 105.5 cm., body H 64.5 cm., 2 bourdon strings and 11 strings on the fingerboard, tuned as follows: c-c'; d-d', g-g', d', a, e', b, f#', c#', g#'. Musikinstrumenten-Museum der Karl-Marx-Universität, Leipzig, 782.

33. LIRA DA BRACCIO

Ventura Linarolo, Venice

Dated 1577

The eminent historian of the violin, David Boyden, has shown that the three parents of the violin are the *lira da braccio,* the Renaissance fiddle (not represented in this exhibition), and the rebec (Nos. 140 and 141). Among those physical characteristics taken from the *lira* are the arched back and belly, their overhang beyond the ribs, the body outline, the usual absence of frets, and (on many specimens) F instead of C sound-holes. Since it was so difficult to construct, the *lira's* soundbox must have had a more pleasing richness and resonance than, say, the rebec's, to justify transposing the *lira's* form to the violin. It is interesting to speculate to what degree the violin appealed to musicians more than the viol because of the convenience of less body depth and the greater ease with which it could be played *da braccio* rather than *da gamba* (along with other advantages and differences, of course).

There are actually very few authentic *liras da braccio* that survive. Two others of special quality and importance are in the Kunsthistorisches Museum, Vienna, and the Ashmolean Museum, Oxford.

H 91.0 cm., body H 60.0 cm., upper bouts W 31.3 cm., centre bouts W 23.5 cm., lower bouts W 40.0 cm. Musikinstrumenten-Museum der Karl-Marx-Universität, Leipzig, 780.

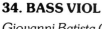

34. BASS VIOL

Giovanni Batista Ciciliano, Venice

circa 1550

The term *viol* is in common use as an abbreviation of *viola da gamba*. The principal ways in which viols differ from members of the violin family are these: all viols are played *da gamba*, have five to seven strings (six is most common) vs. the violin's four, are played with the bow held underhand, are tuned in fourths with one third in the middle vs. the violin's tuning in fifths, have a flat back and sloping shoulders vs. the violin's arched back and quite broad, rounded shoulders, have a deep body vs. the violin's relatively shallow one, rarely have any overhand of back or belly over the ribs and rarely any purfling around these edges, usually have C-shape or flame-shape soundholes vs. the violin's f-holes, and usually have a carved head atop the pegbox rather than the violin's scroll. In addition, the viol fingerboard is wider to accommodate the larger number of strings, and the tailpiece to which the lower ends of the strings are tied is longer. There are internal structural differences as well.

This bass is the oldest viol in the exhibition. Its principal deviation from the characteristics cited above is the scroll above the pegbox, but this is a crude later replacement.

H 107.0 cm., upper bouts W 31.7 cm., centre bouts W 23.0 cm., lower bouts W 35.0 cm., ribs H 12.0 cm. Yale University, Collection of Musical Instruments, New Haven, 127.

35. TENOR VIOL

Ernst Busch, Nürnberg (ca 1590-1650)

Dated 1617

There were indeed luthiers in Nürnberg as well as the celebrated brass and woodwind makers. Busch is, in Jalovec's pontifical words, "a diligent and respected lute and viol maker". This especially handsome body outline is a pattern often used by Busch but not restricted to him. The sound holes are interesting with their squared lower ends. Busch used this shape frequently but not exclusively. The six strings are tuned A, d, g, b, e', a'.

H 90.0 cm., D 12.4 cm., upper bouts W 26.0 cm., centre bouts W 17.8 cm., lower bouts W 30.0 cm., lowest bouts W 27.5 cm. Musikhistorisk Museum og Carl Claudius' Samling, Copenhagen, D 24.

36. CLAVICYTHERIUM

Anonymous, Italian

16th century (?)

Clavicytherium is the name given to upright harpsichords, designed in that form to save space but having the problem of returning the jacks to position for their next note by some other means than gravity. This clavicytherium attempts a solution I have not happened to see elsewhere. The strings themselves run horizontally, which is why the case looks so peculiar, as if its longer strings were at the *right* end rather than the left where convention normally has them. With the strings horizontal, however, the mechanism becomes marvellously simple. Each jack is attached to a long stiff rod that is long enough to place the jack next to its string; the jack rises vertically from the key end and then falls back by gravity after plucking. The string lengths are obviously much shorter than the typical vertically-strung clavicytherium, and yet they are not so thick or overspun, as to produce normal harpsichord pitches.

This then could be an innovative design, but unfortunately it is hard to regard it seriously. The strings themselves appear mounted on a frame and over a soundboard with individual, movable bridges that suggest a large dulcimer standing on its side. The keyboard, while providing the 45 keys for which there are jacks and sets of strings, is mounted in a space too long for it, and the gaps that result at each end are filled by a series of blocks that rise in steps and with rough end-grain toward the player. Most peculiar of all, there are two, three, and even (toward the higher pitches) four strings per note, with no room for additional alternate sets of jacks, and with the two, three, or four strings on the same vertical plane, therefore only the top one in each set is in a position to be affected by the felt damper for which there is a slot in each jack, as usual. To quote the late Raymond Russell at the conclusion of a discussion of Italian forgers of the 19th century, "Anything connected with Italian instruments which does not seem to be in keeping with the style or musical practice of the period, and which is not obvious bona fide renovation or enlargement, must be viewed with suspicion."

H 164.4 cm., W 98.5 cm., D 39.8 cm. Keyboard has 45 keys, with an apparent compass E-c''. The eight lowest pitches are double strung, the next 12 are triple strung, and the upper 25 are quadruple strung. Private collection, Vancouver.

37. VIRGINAL

Domenicus Venetus

Dated 1556

Domenicus Venetus is believed to be another name for Dominicus Pisaurensis, who made our No. 1, and there is no known explanation why he used two names. Donald Boalch's *Makers of the Harpsichord and Clavichord* lists this virginal as No. 7 and raises no question of its authenticity, though some of the instruments attributed to Dominicus may not be his. As I observed in the notes on No. 1 in this exhibition, the span of dates on surviving instruments is too long for all to be by a single individual. The riddle may yet be solved one day.

The virginal is a small type of harpsichord but not always as small and compact as a spinet (No. 1). Like the latter, it has one string per key and therefore lacks the variation in tone afforded by a harpsichord with more than one stop. Also like the spinet, it is primarily a home instrument rather than for large gatherings. Its strings are plucked by crow-quill plectra set into each jack, each jack resting in place on the inner end of each key of the keyboard. The case of this instrument is covered with red velvet. It is unusual that this keyboard does not project from the rest of the case.

L 152.5 cm., D 43.8 cm., case (without legs) H 20.0 cm. One manual: 1 × 8'. Compass 4 octaves, C-c''' with short octave. Yale University Collection of Musical Instruments, New Haven, 241.

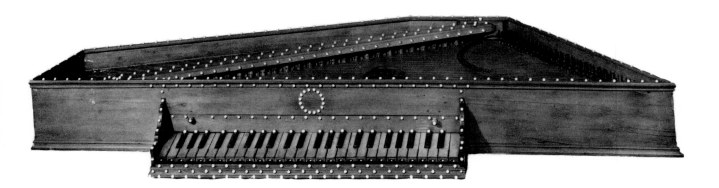

38. SPINETTA

Anonymous, Italian

circa 1560

The term *virginal* is properly reserved for a small harpsichord in rectangular form. I would prefer to call this instrument a spinetta rather than a virginal, although the latter designation is given in the catalogue of the Royal Ontario Museum. It is, then, much like No. 1 in this exhibition and similarly would be kept in an oblong outer case when not in use. Its ivory studs which are purely decorative, were an Italian obsession at this time. They can also be seen in moderation on the preceding virginal. All harpsichords, virginals, and spinets require a jack rail crossing the instrument above the row or rows of jacks, for without this the light jacks would come flying up out the slots which keep them erect and in place. The underside of the jack rail is therefore padded to eliminate the clatter which would otherwise result. The presence of a diagonal jack rail is a good way to distinguish a virginal (which has it) from the also-rectangular clavichord (which does not).

Compass four and a half octaves, C-f''' with short octave. Cypress and cedar. L 156.0 cm. Royal Ontario Museum, Toronto, 913.4.96.

39. OCTAVE VIRGINAL

Anonymous, Augsburg

circa 1600

This beautiful small instrument is found in many collections, usually with more care lavished on the cabinetwork and decoration than on musical quality. It was surely intended as a handsome novelty to sit on a dresser or sideboard, but perhaps there were times when it served as a convenient practice instrument as well.

The case is of ebony with two drawers in the lid; these are too shallow to contain anything but a necklace or something else equally flat. The underside of the lid is decorated with biblical scenes engraved by Crispian van de Passe and Hans Sebald Beham. The natural keys and drawer pulls are of ivory.

Compass three octaves: F-f' omitting F# and G#. H 15.2 cm., W 45.8 cm., D 23.6 cm. Metropolitan Museum of Art, New York, 89.4.1778.

41. HARPSICHORD

Giovanni Celestini, Venice (fl 1583-1610)

Dated 1596

This beautiful instrument may be the finest that has found its way to Canada. There may be other instruments of similar quality and interest in private collections, but if so they have been kept a secret. This is a typical example of one sort of 16th century Italian harpsichord; small, one manual, with two sets of eight-foot strings, separate inner and outer cases, the inner of cypress and cedar. In all probability the outer case is later; its inside lid painting is judged by the Royal Ontario Museum to be early 17th century. The boxwood natural keys have arcaded fronts with a trefoil under each arch, and the accidental keys are stained black. The rose is of wood and parchment.

Actual inscription on name board: *Joannes Celestini Veneti MDXCVI*

Compass four and a half octaves: C-f'' with short octave. H 179.7 cm.
Royal Ontario Museum, Toronto, 913.4.97

The Baroque 1600 1750

No historical epoch, at least in art, responds as well to definition as the Baroque Period in music. The Middle Ages, the gothic, the *Ars Antiqua* and *Ars Nova*, and the early, middle, and late Renaissance can be seen as a single, broad era of remarkable musical development. From the beginning of the "Classical" period in 1750 to well into our own century, there has been another broad era of common practice, even though the modern vocabulary often becomes so rich as to obscure the links with the earlier time. In between, like a massive island barely separating two continents, much bridged but an island nonetheless, is the Baroque Period. Once a term of derision and contempt, not unlike "rococo" and "Victorian" in more recent times, the label "Baroque" now seems singularly satisfactory compared with "Renaissance", for example. Baroque sculpture and architecture (perhaps less so painting) is mirrored in the music of the period (and vice versa) to an unusual degree. As in other ages, music has generally followed other artistic trends at an interval of several decades.

The one device which sets Baroque music apart from that which immediately precedes and follows it is *basso continuo*, the textural element found in all "art music" of the period save that composed for the solo keyboard or unaccompanied string. Rather than the multiple strands of counterpoint that characterize most "art music" before 1600, *basso continuo* involves the use of a prominent bass line, above which the basic "harmony" is supplied unobtrusively by harpsichord or organ, above which play one, two, or sometimes more, featured, melodic instruments - typically voice, violins, flutes, recorders, or oboes and less often violas, a solo cello, bassoon, or trumpet. *Basso continuo* is obviously very similar to the "rhythm section" in jazz. *Basso continuo* was abondoned in the mid-18th century when violas in particular took over the role of filling the "harmony" and providing counter-rhythms between the outer voices. That change marks the end of the Baroque Period and the beginning of the Classical which in turn leads with hardly a ripple to the Romantic era and thence to the 20th century. The change in musical style which marks the beginning of the Baroque followed the logic of developments in the late Renaissance, among the more important of which was the emergence of a group of highly refined instruments. Without these instruments (most notably the violin and the harpsichord), "Baroque music" would simply not have been possible.

Once into the Baroque Period, idiomatic instrumental music gained steadily in importance and appeal; this development was accompanied by improvements in the instruments themselves. This was not only the great period of Italian violin making, the products of which have never been equalled, it was also the age of totally redesigned woodwinds from the Hotteterre and Denner workshops and of the great Nürnberg brass dynasties - Hainlein (No. 19), Ehe (Nos. 21, 22, 108 and 116), Haas (Nos. 112 and 113), and others. One must be careful of a frequent generalization to the effect that the Renaissance made and used *families* of strings and winds (from the sopranino to the great double bass) while the Baroque Period did not. On the contrary, of course, Baroque makers supplied a wide variety of violins and viols, of recorders, of oboes, of trombones, and even of the most important new instrument (excepting the forte-piano) invented in the Baroque period, the clarinet. What is true, and this is where confusion arises, is that in the Baroque era, individual members of each family of instruments were more often used singly and in pairs than in homogenous choirs. To a considerable extent, the Baroque period eventually winnowed out the weaker family members and gave greater prominence to those that remained. We can see this clearly by comparing the number of *types* of surviving instruments by Johann Christoph Denner, who died in 1707, and his son Jakob, who died in 1735.

Opera had its beginnings in the 17th century and it seems paradoxical that this brilliant medium which glorifies the human voice also pioneered the use of new instrumental colours in its orchestras far in advance of their adoption by symphonic composers. In fact, the earliest quasi-orchestral music is generally felt to be that which opens Monteverdi's opera *La Favola d'Orfeo* (1607), and the first use of violin pizzicato and measured tremolo occurs in the same composer's *Combattimento di Tancredi e Clorinda*. Lully, Rameau, Gluck, Mozart, Weber, Berlioz, Meyerbeer, Wagner, and Richard Strauss are among the best known innovators in orchestration, and they more often than not first tried new instruments in their operas. It is almost as if something unusual could be experimented with more successfully if it were buried out of sight in the theatre pit rather than being exposed to visual as well as auditory scrutiny on a concert platform.

For many people, the single instrument that best represents the Baroque Period is the pipe organ. Although the pipe organ was developed much earlier, it was indeed during the Baroque Period that it reached its peak of musical significance. Today, many first-rate Baroque organs are still playable and can be heard in modern recordings. In addition, fine organ builders are presently turning out very impressive "Baroque" models that do full justice to music of that period. Perhaps the most renowned instruments ever produced in Canada are the organs made by Casavant Frères of Quebec.

42. ALTO RECORDER

Johann Christoph Denner, Nürnberg (1655-1707)

The son of a wood-turner who specialized in making animal and bird calls, Denner became, it would appear, the most celebrated woodwind maker in Europe. Today his is perhaps the closest to being a household name among early wind makers. He was said to be a skilled player, and his instruments were admired particularly for their remarkable intonation. According to one account, his sons took entire cases of his instruments to distant parts of Europe even as far as Constantinople and missionaries are said to have carried them even to China. Recorders were a particular specialty.

His instruments are a combination of old and new, some still made in Renaissance form (No. 46, for example, and a recorder very much like No. 3, now in Eisenach), while others reflect the monumental advances introduced by the Hotteterres only a few years earlier. These alto and tenor recorders and the others on succeeding pages are typical Baroque recorders made in three sections (which seemingly simple improvement had any number of advantages), with decorative turnings on the body that are functional as well, and a much more conical bore than in earlier recorders. It is worth noting that 100 years after the Renaissance and two-thirds of the way through the Baroque period, Denner was making recorders in at least six distinct sizes and pitch levels, which challenges the claim that "families" of instruments are purely a Renaissance feature which the Baroque rejected.

Plum, unmounted. L 47.5 cm. Collection of Musical Instruments of Dorothy and Robert Rosenbaum, Scarsdale.

43. TENOR RECORDER

Johann Christoph Denner, Nürnberg (1655-1707)

Plum, ivory mounts. L 65.0 cm. Musik Museet, Stockholm, 1005.

44. BASS RECORDER

Johann Christoph Denner, Nürnberg (1655-1707)

This and the following instrument are characteristic Baroque bass recorders with the same features noted under Nos. 42 and 43 as being among those improvements made by the Hotteterre family and shortly adopted by Denner and others. These, too, are said to be of three-piece construction, but that refers to the body sections that are assembled via tenon and socket joints. The brass crook is also detachable and the head joint (uppermost) is comprised of two separate pieces that come apart for drying and cleaning. These two pieces are a hollow cap at the top that forms a small wind chamber when in place, and the main body of the head joint, which includes the lip or edge against which the breath is directed to set up vibrations in the bore of the instrument. There is one brass key mounted on the foot joint.

Maple, lacquered black, with brass key, mounts, and crook. H 90.0 cm. Institute of Theatre, Music, and Cinematography, Leningrad, 407.

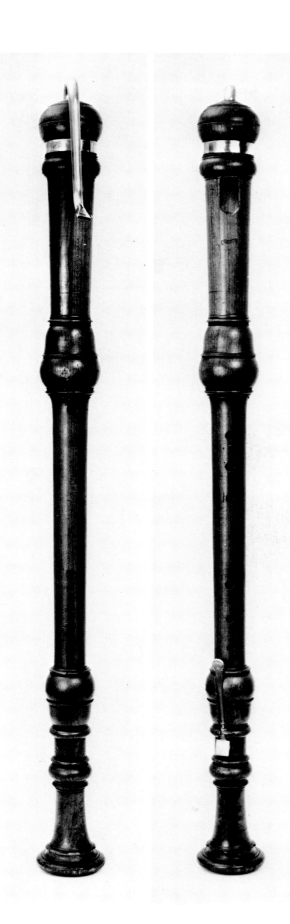

45. BASS RECORDER

Johann Christoph Denner, Nürnberg (1655-1707)

This may be the largest of 28 surviving bass recorders by
Johann Christoph. The crook is a replacement, and the
brass band around the head joint may be also. The one
key is mounted on the foot joint, which can be rotated
thanks to its tenon and socket joint to the main section.
Baroque recorders therefore do not require a swallowtail
key, since the single touch can be turned to accommodate
either left or right hand. Despite this, one sometimes sees a
swallowtail on a low recorder simply following a handsome tradition. Many other woodwinds did not have a
joint at such an ideal place on the body, and so retained a
swallowtail key even into the 19th century, long after it had
become universal practice to play with the right hand
lowermost.

Maple, with brass key, crook, and mount. H 103.3 cm. Bayerisches
Nationalmuseum, Munich, Mu 179.

46. BASS DULCIAN (CHORISTFAGOTT)

Johann Christoph Denner, Nürnberg (1655-1707)

This beautiful instrument was cited a few pages earlier as an example of a Renaissance-type, pre-Hotteterre instrument made by Denner circa 1700. A woodcut published in 1690 in Nürnberg shows a woodwind maker in his workshop surrounded by his tools and an assortment of his products. I like to imagine that this might be Denner himself. At any rate, side by side are dulcians and the new jointed version of the dulcian, the bassoon, which might possibly have been Denner's invention. There do not seem to be earlier ones in existence than the six we know with his stamp (Nos. 47 and 48, among others).

No other Denner instrument is as beautifully engraved as this, which suggests of course that it was made to special order for court use. The two keys are executed in silver as are the perforated boxes that protect them. This *choristfagott* is *gedakt,* (for an explanation of this see No. 12). Finally, what a lovely shape this crook has!

Maple, with silver keys, key covers, crook, and mounts. In C. H 96.4 cm. Germanisches Nationalmuseum, Nürnberg, MI 125.

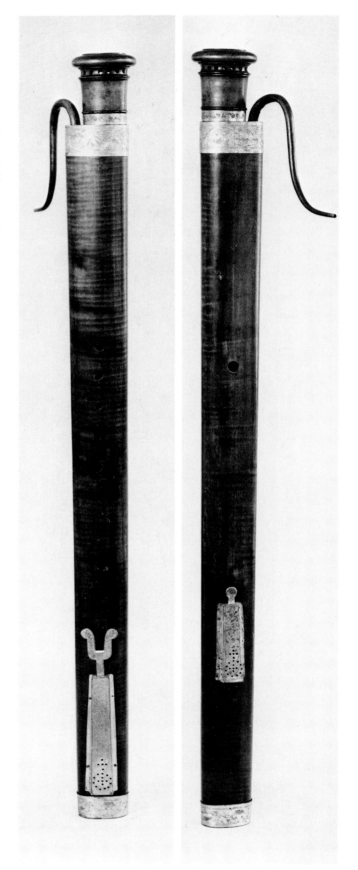

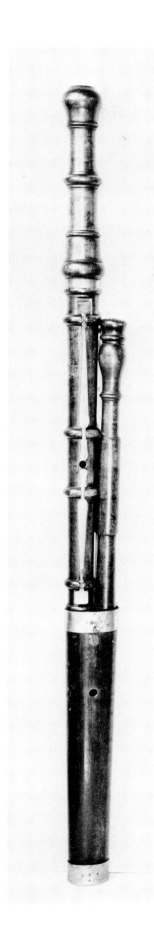

47. BASSOON

Johann Christoph Denner, Nürnberg (1655-1707)

The comments about No. 46 are pertinent as well to the two Denner bassoons in our exhibition. This one from Berlin has three keys, which is characteristic of the earliest form of bassoon, and the fourth key of the following example is almost certainly a later addition. Note the particularly nice swallowtail key shapes on both these instruments and also on the contours of the other keys, which complement the bulbous turnings on these wood bodies (compared with, say, the less ornamented but no less tasteful lines of Heinrich Grenser's bassoon and its keys, no. 193).

The section of any bassoon to which the metal crook is fixed is known as the wing joint because it invariably has a wing-like protruding portion in which are drilled the upper group of three finger holes. This characteristic of all bassoons, today as in Denner's time, permits oblique drilling of the finger holes. On the outer surface, the holes are comfortably spaced for the three fingers, while on the interior surface of the bore (which is all that matters acoustically), the holes, having passed at an angle through the wing, are the proper distance apart to produce the necessary scale tones. This is a superbly simple solution! Many people today believe this feature contributes to the haunting, veiled distant sound of the bassoon. Instruments made with keys in order to eliminate the projecting wing no longer sound like bassoons.

Maple, with brass keys, crook, and mounts. In C. H 120.0 cm. Musikinstrumenten-Museum des Staatlichen Instituts f. Musikforschung-Preussischer Kulturbesitz, Berlin, 2969.

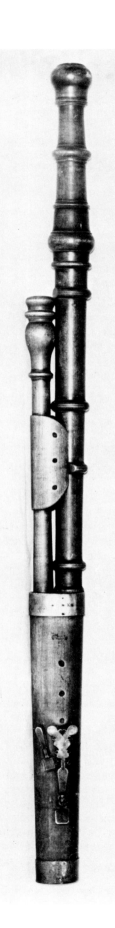

48. BASSOON

*Johann Christoph Denner, Nürnberg
(1655-1707)*

Close scrutiny of the raised turnings on these two Denner bassoons will show very little difference, since they are mainly functional. Some strengthen the sockets of one piece that receive the tenons of another, while others (toward the middle, on the section parallel to the wing joint) are left there as a means of mounting the two long keys. Such key mounts that go completely around the body are known as knobs, while if they are pared down to protrusions on just one side of the tube, they are called blocks. A third type of key mounting is seen here for the swallowtail key, a metal U-shape saddle attached to the body, in which the key pivots on a simple pin as here or, later, on a screw shank. Saddles were used into the 19th century, up to the invention of the posts and axle key mounts used today. Note the letters on the upper band of the boot joint, probably a former owner's initials.

The fourth key on this Leningrad specimen is certainly not original but added later, perhaps even by one of Denner's sons, who were also woodwind makers. Its general shape, especially its touch, is very much in the style of Johann Christoph. Far more often, an added key is poorly executed and without concern for the style of the original keys.

Maple, with brass keys and mounts. In C. H 119.5 cm. Institute of Theatre, Music, and Cinematography, Leningrad, 528.

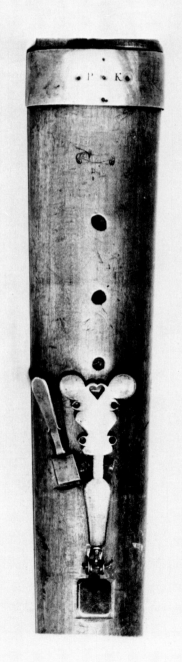

49. FAGOTTINO

Johann Christoph Denner, Nürnberg (1655-1707)

Small-size bassoons are not uncommon, usually being pitched a fourth higher (tenoroon) or an octave higher (octave bassoon), and some were made as recently as the late 19th century. The perplexing thing to the instrument historian is that virtually no music exists for them. The common assumption is that they were made for training young players, whose fingers would have difficulty covering the finger holes on the normal instrument. The fact that, whatever the period in which they were made, they carry all the standard keys and are not simplified versions, may or may not support this.

This is the only *fagottino* in existence by Denner and, but for the less curved crook, is very similar to his full size instruments, Nos. 47 and 48.

Maple, with three brass keys, crook, and mounts. In C. H 63.5 cm. Museum of Fine Arts, Boston, 17.1922.

50. OBOE IN C

Johann Christoph Denner, Nürnberg (1655-1707)

The oboe had been invented by the Hotteterres and put to use at the French court, presumably in 1657. We do not know at what age Denner made his first oboe, but at least eight by him survived into this century, four of which were lost in the Second World War. The eight were evenly divided between the standard c' pitch and the early and short-lived model in d'. *The Look of Music* includes an example of each. This Leningrad specimen is in C and has not been previously illustrated (true of most of the Leningrad instruments in this exhibition), much less seen by students of Western instruments.

This may be the earliest example in this exhibition of eb' duplicate keys, again in order to accommodate whichever hand the player chose to use further from the mouth, combined with a swallowtail touch on the c' great key. The earliest oboes all had these three keys for that reason, and the duplicate eb' was only eliminated by the middle of the century when the right hand found itself permanently assigned to the lower position.

Plumwood? unmounted, with three brass keys. H 56.8 cm. Institute of Theatre, Music, and Cinematography, Leningrad, 508.

51. OBOE IN D

Johann Christoph Denner, Nürnberg (1655-1707)

This slightly shorter oboe is pitched in D but is otherwise very similar to No. 50. The double finger holes seen on both these instruments permit one small hole to be uncovered while the other remains closed, producing a reasonably good sharped note, f# from the fourth finger hole and g# from the third. These instruments, like most oboes for more than 100 years to come, also have two tuning holes at the top of their bells that are never closed and are the immediate source of the instrument's lowest pitch.

Plumwood, unmounted, with three brass keys. H 49.65 cm. Germanisches Nationalmuseum, Nürnberg, MI 155.

53. ALTO RECORDER

Hotteterre

The contributions of instrument makers from this family have been cited often in the preceding pages, but our knowledge of the individuals themselves is scant. A new, intensive study by Marcelle Benoit and Florence Abondance is in press and may fill many of the present gaps. At least five Hotteterres were instrument makers but rarely use an initial or other distinguishing mark (at least that we recognize) on any of the 18 instruments that survive. This recorder has a five-pointed star above and below HOTTETERRE.

One or more of the earlier family members completely redesigned the existing recorder and transverse flute and invented the oboe. To the first two they gave an improved bore, as well as introducing jointed bodies, that is, separable sections. The latter innovation permits adjustment of an instrument's overall pitch — tuning up — before each performance, not practical or possible with a one-piece instrument of Renaissance design. In addition, short sections reduce the incidence of splitting during drilling of the bore, make it less costly to make a replacement section if splitting does occur, permit easier gradation of bore contours for whatever benefit, and so on. The oboe was derived from the centuries-old shawm, and was given a new bore, jointed construction, new key arrangement, and altered reed, resulting in one of the most beautiful instruments of all time.

This alto recorder, like No. 42 by Denner, is the typical Baroque design, of which *The Look of Music* includes a good many. Of all "early" instruments, the alto recorder is the most familiar to avocational players, who will enjoy particularly the slight differences in every dimension and feature as produced by the most celebrated makers during the heyday of the instrument.

Boxwood, finished in imitation tortoise-shell design done with nitric acid, unmounted. 3 sections. H 51.0 cm. Collection of Musical Instruments of Dorothy and Robert Rosenbaum, Scarsdale, 3.

54. ALTO RECORDER

L. Hotteterre

Late 17th century

Three Hotteterre instruments survive with the initial "L" and two have a fleur-de-lys above the initial. The founder of the dynasty was named "Loys", but he is too early (d. 1620?) to have made these particular instruments. The existence of four later family members named "Louis", spanning as many generations, has only recently been discovered, with few clues as to which of them made instruments. The last one died in 1801, which helps to explain a two-keyed oboe that is too late to have been made by the others.

Boxwood with ivory mounts and beak. H 52.5 cm. In three sections. Library of Congress, Washington, D.C., 326.

55. TENOR RECORDER

Hotteterre

As if there were not enough uncertainty and vagueness about Hotteterre stamps, this instrument not only has no initial, it also has the fleur-de-lys of the preceding specimen and its foot joint has two stamps, HOTTETERRE and below that HAUTERRE, the only instance I know of that spelling (clearly seen in the close-up).

Most tenors do not have or require a key, so it is interesting that all three surviving Hotteterre tenor recorders do.

Boxwood?, unmounted, with one brass key. H 68.0 cm. In three sections. Institute of Theatre, Music and Cinematography, Leningrad, 405.

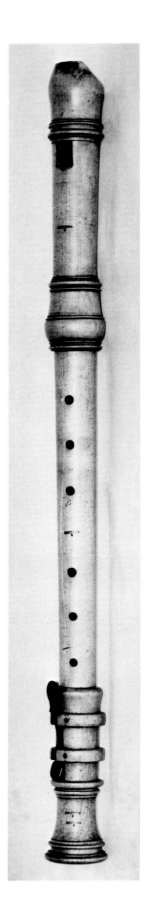

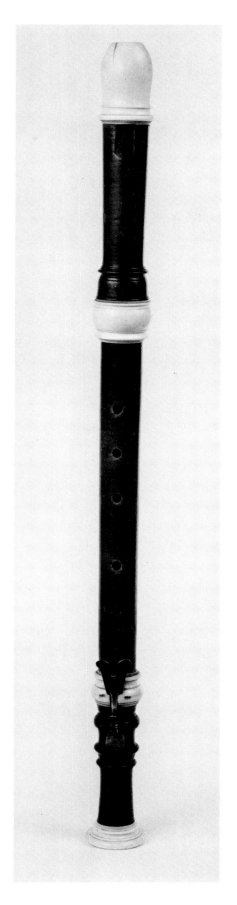

56. TENOR RECORDER

Hotteterre

This instrument has ivory mounts and an ivory beak to break up what would otherwise be a long, bare wooden shape. The swallowtail key touch is nicely proportioned and has a longer "V" than most German instruments. The stamp is HOTTETERRE with an anchor below, the device used on eight of the 16 known Hotteterre instruments, including all four transverse flutes (two of which are Nos. 58 and 59).

Maple, with ivory beak and mounts. One brass key. In three sections. H 68.35 cm. Musée Instrumental du Conservatoire de Paris, E.590, C.402.

57. BASS RECORDER

Hotteterre

This bass recorder has as interesting turnings as any I know, especially the top finial for which there is no explanation other than pure ornamentation. Ignore various sources that state that the Hotteterre stamp here is accompanied by a star or has no device whatever. Instead HOTTETERRE and the anchor (see No. 56) appear on all three sections.

The foot joint is designed to use a floor peg or crutch (missing) to support the instrument at playing height above the floor, hence its lateral port from which the lowest pitch sounds. The brass crook enters the *side* of the head joint, an earlier form than entrance from the *top* (as on the Denner basses, nos. 44 and 45). The swallowtail touch has a decorative centre tine, making a very handsome key.

Maple? with ivory mounts. One brass key. Three sections. H 116.2 cm. (without crutch) Musée Instrumental du Conservatoire de Paris, E.589, C.413.

59. FLUTE IN C

Hotteterre

circa 1700

It has been pointed out that the Hotteterres devised the way (used ever since) to make woodwinds in separate sections, using a simple tenon and socket joint. Whichever of them made the four remaining Hotteterre flutes (see No. 58) had not yet seen a reason for dividing into two the main body section containing the six finger holes, so these instruments have just three sections, a form which didn't occur again until the 19th century.

Maple, with ivory foot joint and mounts. One silver key. L 70.5 cm. Institute of Theatre, Music, and Cinematography, Leningrad, 471.

60. OBOE

N. Hotteterre

circa 1720?

Only two oboes survive with a Hotteterre stamp, and this one has a replacement bell by a little-known 18th century maker, Debey. Michel Piguet, our most gifted performer on the 18th century oboe, dismisses this instrument as too late in style to have been made by any of the "famous" Hotteterres, but I think it could have been made by Nicolas Hotteterre (ca 1646-1727).

The duplicate eb' keys are of the early "dumbbell" shape, more common in the Low Countries, France, and England than east of the Rhine. There is a star above the initial "N" which in turn is above HOTTETERRE.

Boxwood, with ivory mounts. Three brass keys. H 58.8 cm. Musée Instrumental, Brussels, 2320.

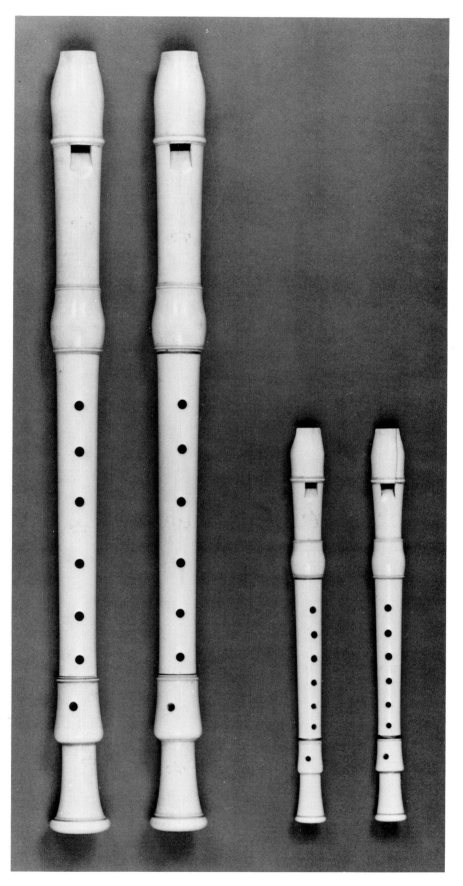

61. SET OF FOUR IVORY RECORDERS

Jeremias Schlegel, Basel (. . .1780-1792)

This handsome set of four instruments — two sopranos and two altos — is unique. For whatever reason, one does not usually find single recorders in fitted cases, much less four. The four are absolutely indistinguishable from each other but for the necessary difference in length between the sopranos and altos; in fact, each soprano is precisely 25.43 cm. long, and the altos are 49.5 and 49.6 cm. respectively.

Anthony Baines has suggested that the set was perhaps intended for duets or trio sonatas, the players having a choice of the two sopranos or the two altos. The set is somewhat of an anachronism, apparently made well after the transverse flute had replaced the recorder in common usage.

Ivory, unmounted. Each recorder made in three sections. Lengths given above. Musée Instrumental du Conservatoire de Paris, E 683, C. 392.

62. SOPRANO RECORDER

I.G. Walch, Berchtesgaden

Early 18th century

The Walchs are an intriguing family of woodwind makers who have been virtually the only makers in this southeastern corner of Bavaria. They worked there continuously from the 17th century well into the 19th. (See also No. 102.) Their collective output is of varied types, to be sure, but there is a decided emphasis on clarinets, recorders and flageolets, all popular to this day in small villages in this breathtakingly beautiful area. The beak and finger holes are worn from hard use.

Maple, unmounted. Foot joint not original. In g'. H 41.0 cm. Museum für Hamburgische Geschichte, Hamburg, 1924.217.

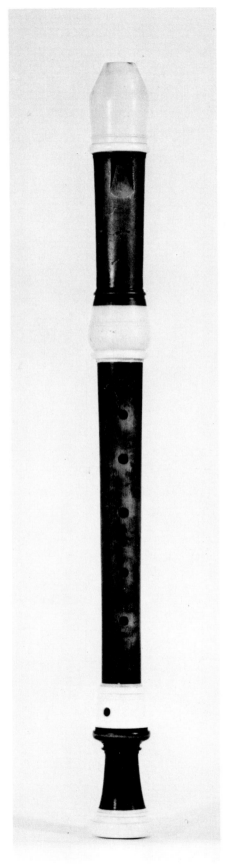

63. ALTO RECORDER

Peter I. Bressan (. . .1683-1735)

Early 18th century

Bressan and the two Thomas Stanesbys, Senior and Junior, are the first important English woodwind makers. The first two of these were contemporaries. Bressan who is believed to have been an immigrant from France in 1683, achieved considerable fame in his lifetime, and his recorders are marvellous playing instruments to this day. He seems to have made only recorders except for three transverse flutes (one of these is our No. 70).

Boxwood, with ivory beak and mounts. In three sections. In F. H 50.3 cm. Library of Congress, Washington, D.C., 127.

64. ALTO RECORDER

I.W. Oberlender II, Nürnberg (1712-1779)

Highly carved recorders such as this, and particularly altos, are a specialty of the Oberlenders, father and son, and another important Nürnberg recorder maker, Johann Benedikt Gahn. Often such carved recorders are in the form of flamboyant fish, and at other times not, as here. What is the significance of the woeful expression, eyes cast imploringly heavenward?

Boxwood, unmounted. In three sections. In F. H 50.0 cm. Collection of Musical Instruments of Dorothy and Robert Rosenbaum, Scarsdale, 2.

65. ALTO RECORDER

Jean-Hyacinth-Joseph Rottenburgh, Brussels (1672-1765)

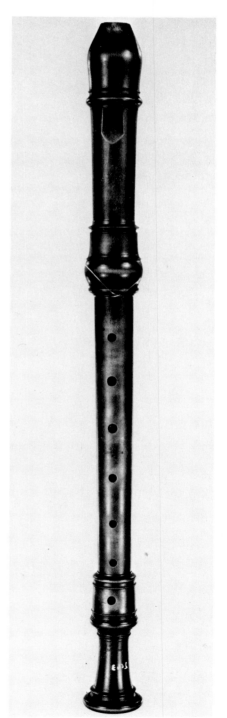

The Rottenburghs are the great family of Belgian wind instrument making. The maker of this alto recorder (and also Nos. 91 and 95) is the most important, but his son Godefroid-Adrien was also a skilled maker. As always, it is instructive to note the changing taste and needs of an era as reflected in the respective output of two or more generations of a family, whether they are Denners, Hotteterres, Oberlenders, Stanesbys, or Saxes. The Rottenburghs have another illustrious family member in the person of Victor Charles Mahillon, the great grandson of J.-H.-J.R., who became a major 19th-early 20th century organologist and acoustician, instrument collector, and Conservateur of the great Musée Instrumental du Conservatoire Royal de Musique de Bruxelles, today still the largest collection in the world, and the one from which this and a great many other unique specimens have been loaned to *The Look of Music.*

To modern recorder players the name Rottenburgh is primarily associated with the fine copy of an instrument similar to this, designed by the noted Boston maker Friedrich von Huene, and produced on a large scale by Moeck, of Celle, West Germany. The instrument is known around the world as their "Rottenburgh model".

Pearwood, unmounted. In F. L 50.0 cm. Musée Instrumental, Brussels, 2643a.

66. TENOR RECORDER

Charles Bizey, Paris (. . .1716-1752. . .)

This is one of only two known recorders by an important French maker who otherwise specialized in flutes and a wide assortment of double reeds (Nos. 92, 96, and 106). An interesting feature here is the unusual shape of the upper bulge of the foot joint, usually where the seventh fingerhole is found but here covered instead by a brass key hinged from its lower end. The key itself has a chamfer on the flap edges in a design I've not seen previously. The photo detail shows this and Bizey's characteristic stamp very clearly. The mounts are as described below, not bone as incorrectly given in the Blagodatov catalogue.

Black lacquered boxwood, with ivory beak and mounts. In three sections. In C. H 67.4 cm. Institute of Theatre, Music, and Cinematography, Leningrad, 404.

67. BASS RECORDER

Thomas Boekhout, Amsterdam (1665-1715)

Here is an example of a floor crutch used to support a bass recorder in playing position, (missing in No. 57). Bressan (No. 63) probably uses the crutch more often than any other maker of bass recorders. A more interesting feature here, however, is the use of a second key, in place of and set lower than the usual third finger hole. This puts the hole in a more acoustically correct (in tune) location. I do not know of another instance of such a key so early. That it is mounted in blocks which appear to be integral rather than added later, proves that the key was Boekhout's innovation.

Black lacquered (?) boxwood, with brass crook and keys. In three sections plus crook. H 142.0 cm. with crutch. Institute of Theatre, Music, and Cinematography, Leningrad, 408.

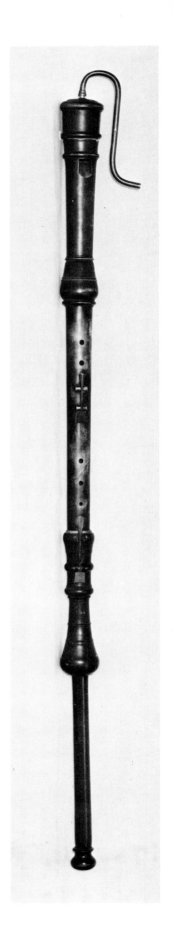

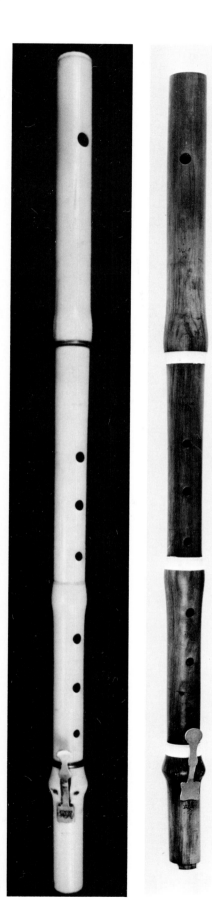

68. TWO TRANSVERSE FLUTES IN CASE

Thomas Lot, Paris (. . .1740-1785)

In all, this set includes two head joints, ten upper joints, two lower joints, and one foot joint with another clearly missing. They are, then, two flutes, each with five upper joints (see explanation below) and are reminiscent of the handsome, similar set in the Carse Collection, if not quite as elegant. The flute with the inventory number Mu 172 has from one to five dots *above* the maker's name on each upper joint, while the flute Mu 176 has its distinguishing one to five dots *below* the maker's stamp. Mu 176 is the one with missing foot joint. Both flutes' head joint caps are lost. A slight variation in the colour of finish of various sections would suggest that the flutes may have been assembled with an upper joint from the other and left for quite some time thus assembled, but the dots clearly differentiate the two instruments as originally made.

Thomas Lot is an important Parisian maker, also represented in *The Look of Music* by Nos. 72 and 94. The beauty of execution is quite striking on every instrument with his stamp. The key motif used on these two flutes is an example of this and is also, I believe, a unique design.

Tulipwood (?), with ivory mounts. One silver key. Each flute made in four sections. Mu 172 L 65.7 cm. with upper joint #1, Mu 176 length not given because of missing footjoint. Case: Black leather covered, with silver mounts and handle. H 9.5 cm. × 30.3 cm. × 27.0 cm. Bayerisches National-museum, Munich, Mu 172, Mu 176.

69. IVORY FLUTE

John Just Schuchart, London (. . .1720-1759)

Dr. Maurice Byrne has made an important study of Schuchart, who seems to have immigrated to London from Germany at the earlier of the two dates above. His son Charles was born in that same year and eventually took over the family workshop. He was succeeded by Thomas Collier, an important maker in his own right.

Flutes in hard, fitted cases were fairly common at this time, more so than in either the 17th or 19th centuries, undoubtedly because of the frequency with which alternate upper joints were provided. Such alternate upper joints were less common for clarinets, oboes, and bassoons, for which cases are rarely preserved.

Ivory, with silver key and mounts. In four sections. Key has (one-time owner's?) monogram "DCM". L 63.6 cm. with longest of three upper joints. Bate Collection, Oxford, 101.

70. FLUTE

Peter J. Bressan, London (. . .1683-1735)

Bressan made recorders principally (see No. 63), but three of his flutes exist which are important links between the earliest jointed flutes of the Hotteterres (Nos. 58 and 59) and late Baroque instruments (Nos. 68, 69, 71, and 85). One should compare this one with all those to see the evolution of flute design in the 18th century that leads to the Grensers and Kirst, then to Stephan Koch and Boehm.

Dr. Dayton C. Miller (1866-1941) was a distinguished acoustician and professor of physics, who amassed the largest collection of flutes ever assembled. He later gave the collection, and his papers and library of documents relating to the flute, to the Library of Congress. How he acquired this rare Bressan flute is best told by Dr. William Lichtenwanger, the curator-emeritus of the collection:

"It would be hard to imagine a less likely place for a Bressan flute than the thieves' market in the Mexican town of Toluca whence came the specimen here concerned, this specimen having been spotted and acquired for Dr. Miller by three intermediaries among whom was the then Chief of Police in Los Angeles. The flute reached Dr. Miller at his Cleveland home in February 1934. He immediately realized what a prize he had acquired, for in his letter of thanks to his agent. . ." etc.

Boxwood, with ivory mounts. One silver key now mounted on metal staple, originally was mounted in knob. L 62.7 cm. Library of Congress, Washington, D.C., 1207.

72. BASS FLUTE

Thomas Lot, Paris (. . .1740-1785)

This bass flute, unfortunately the only one in *The Look of Music,* is a particularly handsome specimen by a maker whose instruments always reflect a very high standard of workmanship. (See also Nos. 68 and 94.) The design of the four unusual keys (instead of finger holes 1,3,4 and 6) is like that used by Lot on the other known bass flute by him (now Brussels No. 175), by Bizey on a very similar bass flute in Linz, presumably slightly earlier, and even by Adolphe Sax a hundred years later on his bass clarinet. These keys are hinged at one end, have a bulge in their centre to which a pad is attached to cover the actual hole in the tube, with the "touch" at the other end at a comfortable spot for the finger. The whole purpose, of course, is to allow the finger to close a key so placed as to be in the acoustically correct position, which would otherwise lie beyond reach of that finger. Such keys are in fact "second class" levers. The fifth key is of conventional design for eb.

Maple, with ivory mounts. Five brass keys. Made in five sections, with brass 'U' between head joint and the main four-section body. L 102.5 cm. Institute of Theatre, Music, and Cinematography, Leningrad, 473.

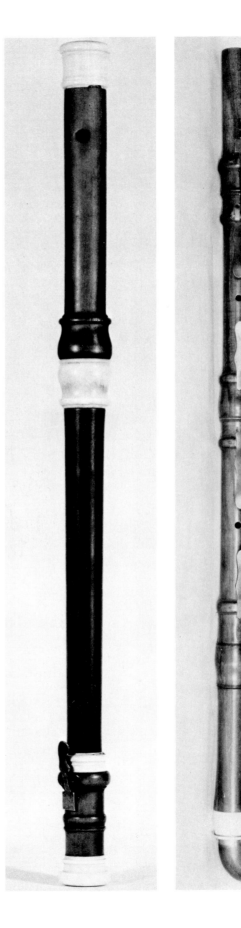

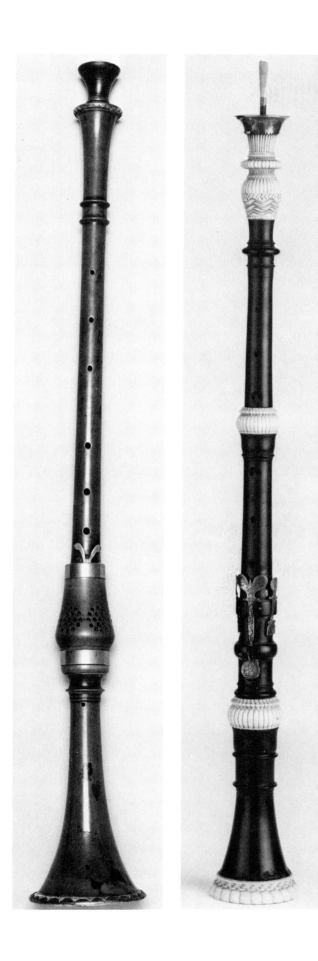

73. DEUTSCHE SCHALMEI

Richard Haka, Amsterdam (1645-1705)

One of the glaring holes in woodwind history is our lack of much knowledge of the group of makers, especially and most importantly of oboes, that seems to have suddenly appeared in Amsterdam about 1670. For a hundred years they produced oboes as beautiful as any to be found, as well as a limited number of other types. Then suddenly, at least in terms of continental importance, they disappeared. Their relationship, and particularly their earliest members' relationship, to the Hotteterres is a complete enigma. Very early Hotteterre oboes do not seem to survive, nor do oboes from a second generation of French makers, yet a considerable number of Amsterdam oboes from that time are preserved. These general observations pertain to this instrument and the next four, which have been grouped together so that they can be surveyed with the admiration they deserve.

Richard Haka, interestingly enough, was of English birth but came with his parents to settle in Amsterdam when he was five years old. His father was a cane-maker, another trade for which the woodturning lathe is a principal tool. A single, one-keyed instrument of his, now in the Hague City Museum, is the earliest oboe or transitional shawm-oboe that is known. In addition he is represented by several other oboes as well as a number of examples of the modified shawm known as a *Deutsche schalmei*. This latter, unlike the present specimen, normally has no key, only a perforated wooden fontanelle covering a vent hole. The key on our instrument was added later. The *Deutsche schalmei* is another, late attempt, coming just after the invention of the oboe, to refine the centuries-old shawm and give it at least some of the delicacy and expressiveness that had immediately won a place for the new oboe. It was too late; the oboe was too good and the *schalmei* was discarded except by village bands in rural areas.

Boxwood, with brass band around pirouette at top, around top of main section, around both edges of fontanelle, and around bell rim. Made in two sections, Renaissance-style: main joint and bell. Four tuning holes in bell. H 65.4 cm. Yale University Collection of Musical Instruments, New Haven, 438.

74. OBOE

Hendrik Richters, Amsterdam (1683-1727)

In roughly the middle of the 100-year period of Dutch oboe makers cited under No. 73, came Hendrik Richters whose instruments must be among the most elegant and most beautiful ever made. A younger brother Frederick (Jr.) worked with and after him in the same style and at the same level of craftmanship. For all its richness, his ornamentation is always tasteful and appears set off like a jewel against the flawless simplicity of the clean-lined bodies of ebony. It is startling each time one recalls how rarely in the four centuries covered by this exhibition are woodwind key surfaces engraved or ivory mounts carved with any design but rings turned on a lathe.

Ebony, with ivory rings and top finial. Silver cap over top flare of ivory finial. Three silver keys. H 56.7 cm. Haags Gemeentemuseum, Holland, Ea 548-1933.

75. OBOE

Hendrik Richters, Amsterdam (1683-1727)

A similar and as equally lovely an instrument as No. 73. The close-up details show how fine the key engraving and ivory carving are. This particular Hendrik Richters oboe has much less enigmatic engraving than many others. The touch of the great key has a dancing (?) couple pulling each other in opposite directions, while the right-hand eb touch shows a wind player (perhaps an oboist) and the left touch a string player.

The engraving on the previous specimen, No. 74, is in fact more enigmatic and in that way more typical. Its great key touch has a barrel, a winged hour-glass, and a diagonal ladder above an orb or glove surmounted by a cross. This is the same rebus as appears on a Richters oboe owned by Guy Oldham, London, who deciphered it as meaning (in Dutch): *Grasp time and learn the world to know.* Many of the same symbols are used in different combinations on other Richters oboes.

Ebony, with ivory rings and top finial. Three silver keys. H 57.2 cm. Metropolitan Museum of Art, New York, 53.56.11.

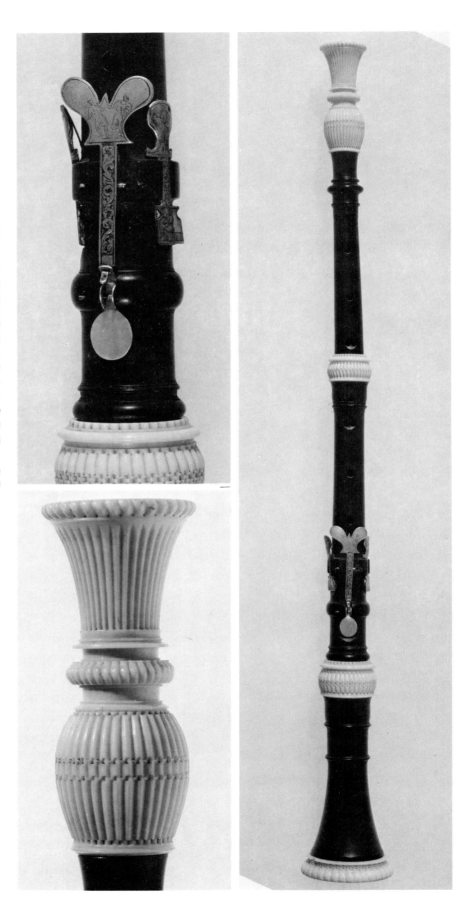

76. OBOE

*Thomas   Boekhout,   Amsterdam
(1665-1715)*

This maker was mentioned earlier for
his bass recorder No. 67, but all attempts to learn more of his life have
failed. While more of his recorders
survive than any of his other instruments, this is one of two handsome
oboes of his from the Hague, and a
two-keyed clarinet now in Brussels is
one of the very earliest we have after
those made by J.C. Denner.

Boxwood, unmounted. Three brass keys. H
58.0 cm. Rijksmuseum, Amsterdam, Ea 16-X-
1952.

77. TENOR OBOE

Hendrik Richters, Amsterdam (1683-1727)

I remember laughing aloud the first time I saw this instrument. Is is unmistakably Hendrik Richters in proportions, style, and excellence of workmanship, but it is as if the usual and expected Richters decoration — engraved key surfaces and beautifully carved ivory — had been scrubbed away by one of those sombre, black-suited Calvinistic-Dutch burghers we know from endless 17th century portraits. What is surprising too is that the name on all three sections is enclosed in a ribbon-like scroll, often used in other makers' stamps but not otherwise by Hendrik Richters, to my knowledge. It might suggest a different maker of this name, but the instrument itself belies that possibility.

Boxwood, with ivory mounts. Three brass keys. H 84.5 cm. Musée Instrumental du Conservatoire de Paris, E. 1185, C.1116.

78. OBOE

Jakob Denner, Nürnberg (1681-1735)

Jakob Denner is not without distinction in his own right. While he actually invented no new instrument, he kept abreast of others' innovations, making transverse flutes, oboes *d'amore,* and if an older label is to be trusted, even an oboe *da caccia,* none of which his father is known to have made, as well as three sizes of recorder, clarinets, oboes, and bassoons. The wonder is that there are not more surviving woodwinds by Jakob, whose working period presumably extended 28 years beyond his father's death, but whose instruments number slightly more than half his father's known examples. The height of this oboe is more that of a *d'amore,* but its bell is flared. It has not been possible to check its pitch before this catalogue went to press.

Boxwood, unmounted. Three brass keys. H 61.3 cm. Institute of Theatre, Music, and Cinematography, Leningrad, 1135.

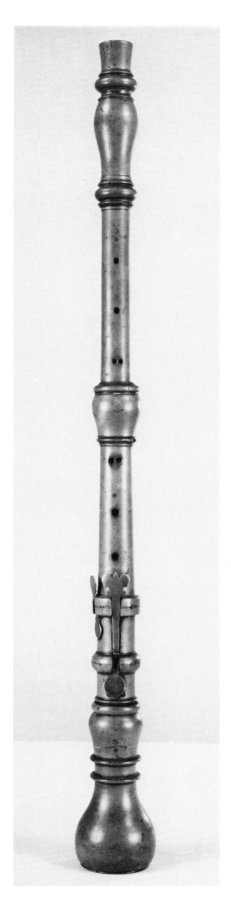

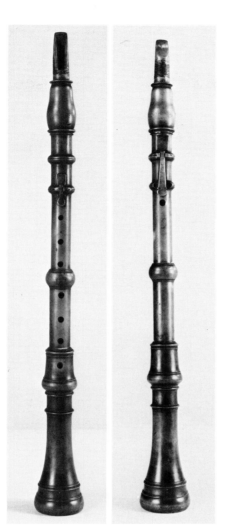

79. CLARINET

Jakob Denner, Nürnberg (1681-1735)

After Johann Christoph's *chalumeau* (No. 52), this is the next Denner model that we have been able to include in *The Look of Music*. It is by virtue of its four sections already later than other Jakob three-section clarinets, of which Nürnberg MI 149 is the only surviving example. This by any accepted definition is a true clarinet, flared bell and all. The Klenig (No. 98) is earlier and properly a *chalumeau,* in modern terminology. There is still no Denner clarinet by either father or son with more than two keys, although efforts continue (and, I understand, will be published in the Galpin Society *Journal,* Vol. XXXIII) to declare a Berkeley specimen such a major discovery.

Boxwood, unmounted. Two brass keys. Speaker key hole is higher and of smaller diameter than a' key hole, unlike earlier Denner models. H 60.0 cm. Bore 1.43-1.47 cm. Musée Instrumental, Brussels, 912.

80. OBOE D'AMORE

Johann Heinrich Eichentopf, Leipzig (1678-1769)

The next nine instruments are of special significance. They were made in Leipzig and, in all likelihood, during the 27-year period that Johann Sebastian Bach served as cantor of the Thomasschule. The several makers (and there were not many others working in Leipzig at that time) would certainly have known Bach, some very likely would have made instruments for use at the Thomaskirche, and at least one is said to have designed a "new" instrument with Bach's encouragement and help, and to have been a close personal friend. It is reasonable to suppose that some of these very instruments were heard by the great man.

The oboe *d'amore* is an alto oboe in a, a minor third lower than the soprano oboe, and fitted with a globular, pear-shaped bell that gives it a slightly veiled quality. The instrument originated in the late Baroque and probably in Leipzig, and no other maker made so many in proportion to his other surviving instruments as Johann Heinrich Eichentopf. The frequency with which Bach wrote for it in works of the Leipzig period confirms his special fondness for it.

Boxwood, unmounted. All three sections have Eichentopf stamp, contrary to published reports. Two brass keys. H 61.1 cm. without staple. Musée Instrumental, Brussels, 971.

81. OBOE D'AMORE

Johann Heinrich Eichentopf, Leipzig (1678-1757)

In the remarkable series of recordings of Bach cantatas performed by the *Concentus Musicus* of Vienna using "original" instruments, the cantatas that make up the Christmas Oratorio are a special joy and include many passages for two oboes *d'amore* and alternately for two oboes *da caccia*. The latter are heard in this recording for the first time in this century, in fact probably since the 18th century, thanks to two copies of No. 83 (or its near duplicate and the only other Eichentopf *da caccia* in existence, in the Stockholm Musik Museet) made by a former member-oboist of *Concentus Musicus,* Paul Hailperin. The remarkably beautiful sound of these pairs of instruments is just one more dynamic, convincing example of why music should be played on the exact instruments for which it was originally written.

Bach did indeed write very beautifully for the soprano oboe and Eichentopf did indeed make them as well as *d'amores* and *da caccias,* but neither of two surviving Eichentopf oboes are in a very good state of conservation or appearance and so were not sought for this exhibition. (They look very much like No. 78 by Jakob Denner, in fact.) Oboes *d'amore* (but not *da caccias,* as yet) are once again being manufactured by some of the major firms, as well as by individual artist-craftsmen.

Maple or boxwood, unmounted but for horn ring used as later repair. Two brass keys. H 61.1 cm. Musée Instrumental du Conservatoire de Paris, E.205, C.473

82. OBOE D'AMORE

Johann Poerschman, Leipzig (1680-1769)

This oboe *d'amore* is very much like Eichentopf's (Nos. 80 and 81), but there are slight differences that are interesting to see. Poerschman's bell is more "pear" and less round than Eichentopf's, for example, and the key shapes offer an opportunity for varying design and personal taste.

Poerschman (that is the way *he* spells the name, not as it is given in MGG or Langwill) is an intriguing but shadowy maker of whom we must try to learn more. He is best known today as the teacher of two major makers of the next generation, August Grenser and Jakob Grundmann, but his own surviving instruments are of interest, if too few in number to afford as much perspective. This *d'amore* may be the major item. There is a paradox perhaps in his (as opposed to Eichentopf) having whatever it took to attract young August and Jakob as apprentices, yet being represented by so singularly few instruments in collections today. He was an excellent bassoonist, the first principal bassoon of the newly formed Leipzig Gewandhaus Orchestra in fact, as well as an occasional oboist. Perhaps he drew apprentices more as a performer who also made instruments than strictly by the latter activity alone. Perhaps his bassoons and various types of oboe played so well that this attracted the two apprentices to him.

Black stained maple (?), unmounted, Two brass keys. H 62.9 cm. Metropolitan Museum of Art, New York, 89.4.2091.

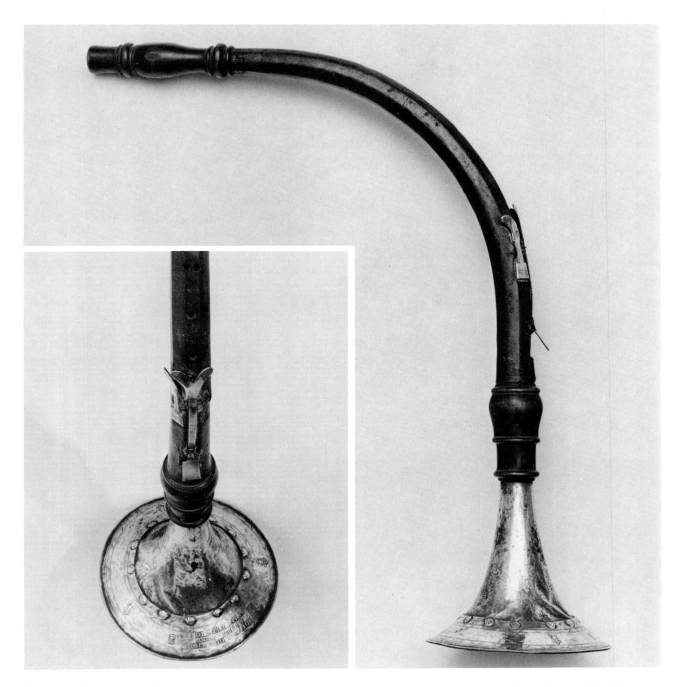

83. OBOE DA CACCIA

Johann Heinrich Eichentopf, Leipzig (1678-1769)

Dated 1724

Two oboes *da caccia* by Eichentopf exist, both dated 1724 and both in Scandinavian museums today. It is difficult not to think of them as a matched pair, as they are so alike in every detail; also, this instrument's principal use is in pairs in certain cantatas by Johann Sebastian Bach. (See the remarks accompanying oboe *d'amore* No. 81.) The oboe *da caccia* is pitched in f and is a kind of tenor oboe with a curved tube and widely flared bell of either wood or metal. The term "tenor oboe" or *taille* is today reserved for a straight-bodied oboe in f (Nos. 89 and 92-95, for example), whether with bulb bell or flared. No one has claimed that the oboe *da caccia* is visually a thing of great beauty. Many tenor oboes are.

The tonal quality of the *da caccia* is certainly not the same as a modern English horn's, even though they are made at the same pitch and the latter is therefore easily substituted for the former in modern times. Few would dispute the claim that the English horn is the superior, more versatile instrument, but what an indescribable thrill to hear a pair of true *da caccias* playing Bach!

Boxwood covered with black leather, unmounted. Brass bell and three brass keys. L 84.2 cm. along outside of curve. Bell dia. 16.2 cm. Musikhistorisk Museum og Carl Claudius' Samling, Copenhagen, E-70.

84. ALTO RECORDER

Johann Poerschman, Leipzig (1680-1757)

This typical Baroque recorder is nicely made and said to play very well. It is quite impressive that so many beautiful and truly rare instruments are preserved in Scandinavian collections. The instrument museums of Stockholm and Copenhagen are particularly important and rank among the great collections anywhere.

Boxwood, unmounted. H49.0 cm. Musikhistorisk Museum og Carl Claudius Samling, Copenhagen, 417.

85. FLUTE IN Eb (?)

Johann Poerschman, Leipzig (1680-1757)

The Look of Music includes three of the five complete instruments by Poerschman that are known to exist. Two pieces only of other specimens also survive. These statistics prompt the earlier (see No. 82) speculation about Poerschman's being more active as a player than a maker. This small flute is as beautifully made as any of the other five specimens by Poerschman, but the most remarkable thing about it is its pitch, not a common size at that time.

Boxwood, with ivory mounts. One silver key. In four sections. L 50.8 cm. Institute of Theatre, Music, and Cinematography, Leningrad, 453.

86. BASSOON

Johann Heinrich Eichentopf, Leipzig (1678-1769)

This bassoon is remarkable among other things for its clean lines and exterior profile, in marked contrast to the heavy, more Baroque turnings of Denner bassoons. The handsome brass band around the bell end is both decorative and protective, a feature to be seen on many post-Denner bassoons by Poerschman, August Grenser, and Kirst, among others. All other Eichentopf bassoons have the same smooth exterior, whether he, Poerschman, Scherer, or someone else (in England?) was the first to use it in preference to the heavily turned form.

Maple, with four brass keys (Bb,D,F, and G#), brass crook and mounts. H 126.9 cm. Germanisches Nationalmuseum, Nürnberg, MI 127.

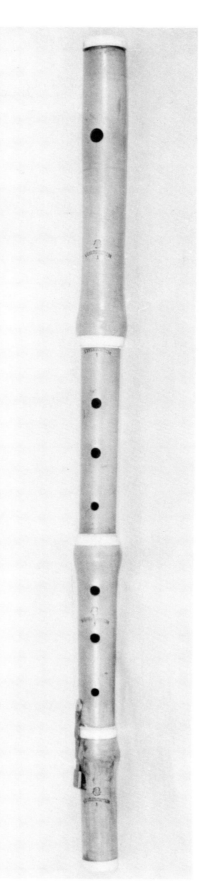
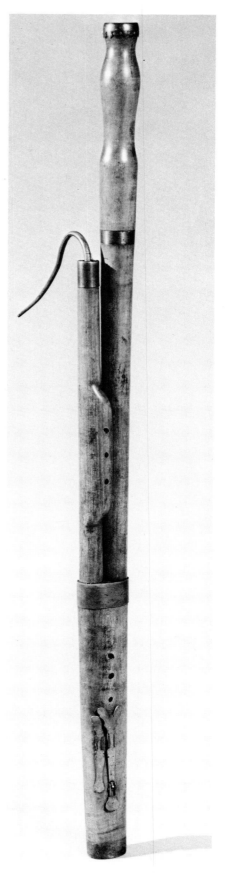

87. VIOLA POMPOSA

Johann Christian Hoffmann, Leipzig (1683-1750)

Dated 1732

Tradition has it that Bach either invented this instrument himself or suggested it to his close friend Hoffmann, a noted luthier, but there has been considerable and widespread questioning of this in recent years. One school of thought believes that Bach was frustrated by the limitations of cellists and double bassists of the time and sought a substitute that was low-pitched, but could be played at the shoulder or neck with more rapid fingering thus possible. Others point to the fact that no Bach score contains the designation *viola pomposa,* even if certain works by

Graun and Telemann do. Jürgen Eppelsheim has made a very convincing argument that the *viola pomposa* was intended to play with the celli, reading the cello part and taking over entirely any time the line became too rapid for cello execution.

What has not been clear in other published photographs of Hoffmann *violas pomposa* known to me is the extraordinary depth of the ribs of this specimen, at least, and perhaps of others as well. No. 149 is not nearly so deep, even though made at a later date and by an anonymous maker.

Tuning: C,G,d,a,e' (as given for this specific instrument by Kinsky in the Heyer Collection *Kleiner Katalog*) Overall L. 77.0 cm. Body L. 45.0 cm. Upper bouts, 21.5 cm. Middle bouts 15.1 cm. Lower bouts 27.0 cm. Musikinstrumenten Museum der Karl-Marx-Universität, Leipzig, 918.

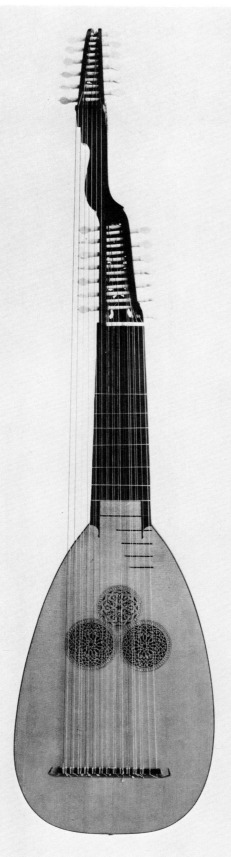

88. THEORBO

Johann Christian Hoffman, Leipzig (1683-1750)

Dated 1720

The lute and its extended version, the *theorbo,* outlived the Renaissance and even the 17th century, enjoying a final period of activity in Germany in the first half of the 18th century. Bach wrote for the lute at least and, if only to judge from the existence of several *theorbos* by his friend Hoffmann, must have seen that instrument used in Leipzig as well. This instrument, which is in perfect condition, is one of two by Hoffman in the Musikinstrumenten Museum, Leipzig. Another is in Berlin. All three have a triple rose.

The *theorbo* strictly speaking is a lute with an appreciably lengthened neck and two pegboxes, one roughly half the distance away from the body as the other, the first with strings whose pitch and function are the same as on the ordinary lute and the second, lying off to one side, with much longer strings that provide a single bass note. It is similar, then, to the *chitarrone* (Nos. 25 and 26) but for the fact that the neck and bass strings of the *chitarrone* are even longer. One must be aware that *chitarrone* and *theorbo* have both been used in earlier times to specify any long-necked lute. Today, however inconsistent it may be with earlier meanings, the terms are widely used as stated.

Overall L. 147.0 cm. Body L. 55.0 cm. Body maximum W. 33.3 cm. Twelve double courses, two single. Musikinstrumenten Museum der Karl-Marx-Universität, Leipzig, 506.

89. TENOR OBOE

Thomas Stanesby, Junior, London (1692-1754)

There is at best an honest simplicity and plainness about this particular instrument, but in this and other ways it is representative of its type. During the 18th century the tenor oboe took this form in England, and there is a shorter-lived "English straight model" of the standard oboe (No. 169) characterized by similarly stark lines save for a bell that flares considerably more. The English tenor was known as *Vox Humana,* and the late Eric Halfpenny has suggested that the familiar organ stop of that name is far more likely to be named for the tenor oboe than for any similarity to the human voice.

The Stanesbys, father and son, are the earliest English woodwind makers of importance but for Bressan, an immigrant from France in 1683. Stanesby instruments are normally very beautifully made, and one writer has suggested that this particular tenor oboe might have been made by a mere apprentice.

Cedar (?), with brass crook and mount. Two brass keys. H 76.5 cm. without crook. Victoria and Albert Museum, London, 291-1882.

90. OBOE

Thomas Stanesby, Senior, London (. . .1706-1734)

This lovely instrument is the classic English three-keyed oboe that Handel would have heard upon arrival in England and for which he wrote so beautifully again and again. Like No. 53, its boxwood has been stained in imitation of tortoise shell by the use of nitric acid. Its broad, handsomely turned ivory mounts are nicely set off against the darkened wood, while its neat, silver keys are a pleasing complement to the whole.

Stained boxwood, with ivory mounts. Three silver keys. H 58.9 cm. Collection of Musical Instruments of Dorothy and Robert Rosenbaum, Scarsdale, 57.

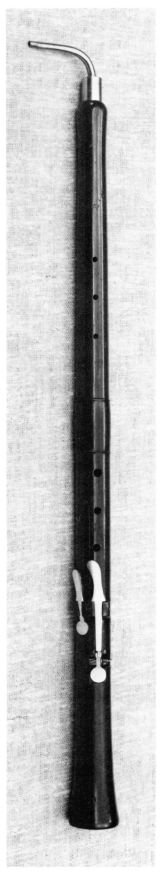

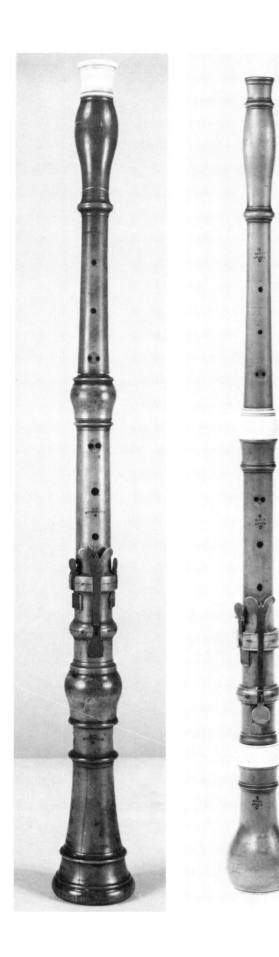

91. OBOE

Jean-Hyacinth-Joseph Rottenburgh, Brussels (1672-1765)

This important Baroque maker is discussed under No. 65. It is interesting that he is survived by a number of both two-keyed and three-keyed oboes; so in fact is his son, who died in 1790. The father made no clarinets whatever as far as I know, while the son made a great many.

Michel Piguet has recorded as well as concertized in both hemispheres, using his "I.H. ROTTENBURGH" three-keyed oboe, which is his single favourite instrument of a number of beautiful old ones in his collection. (The name as given above in capitals is the way the maker stamped his instruments, with a six-pointed star below.)

Boxwood, with ivory mounts. Three brass keys (2Xeb). In C. H 59.9 cm. Musée Instrumental, Brussels, 2608.

92. TENOR OBOE

Charles Bizey, Paris (. . .1716-1752. . .)

It is interesting to compare this tenor oboe by an important French maker with a German tenor (No. 93) made by an equally respected, exact contemporary. The difference between two keys on one and three on the other is not significant; curiously enough, the tenor oboe tended to stabilize the right hand in the lowermost position earlier than the soprano oboe. (All Johann Christoph Denner's oboes have three keys vs. only two on his tenors and baritones, and this was several decades earlier than the Bizey instruments illustrated here.) Beyond that difference, the body lines are quite different, the French having a slimmer, cleaner appearance vs. the more Baroque turning on the German instrument. The lighter profile of the French model is actually much more graceful and balanced, while the bell of the German oboe seems disproportionately heavy in comparison. Given such a special opportunity to compare appearance, it would be fascinating to compare their respective sounds.

Boxwood, with ivory mounts. Two brass keys. H 73.2 cm. Musée Instrumental du Conservatoire de Paris, E.2351.

93. TENOR OBOE

Johann Wolfgang Kenigsperger, Roding (?) (- 1752)

The Musik Museet in Stockholm owns a matched, identical pair of these, a decided rarity although oboes *d'amore* and basset horns are frequently preserved in pairs in other museums. I suggested earlier (see No. 83) that even the very similar oboes *da caccia* by Eichentopf in Copenhagen and Stockholm, each dated 1724, might have been a pair originally. As opposed to *da caccias*, straight tenors seem to be called for singly in much music, as a middle voice with a pair of oboes on top and a bassoon as bass.

Kenigsperger is believed to be the second in a three-generation family of woodwind makers. His father spelled the name "Kinigsperger" and his son (?) "Königsperger". The maker of this tenor oboe is the more important and is survived by more instruments than either of the others.

Plumwood, with stained boxwood bell, unmounted. Three brass keys. H 70.35 cm. Musik Museet, Stockholm, No. 1007.

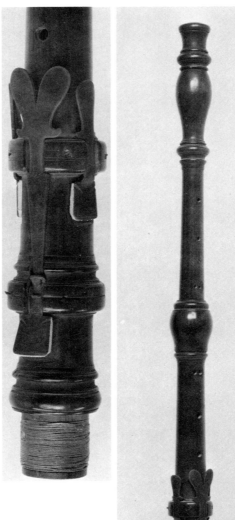

94. TENOR OBOE

Thomas Lot, Paris (. . .1740-1785)

There are many similarities in form between this tenor and the earlier one, also French, by Bizey (No. 92), but this one has a flared rather than bulb bell. There is a wonderful story of a modern London professional who specialized in English horn and who eventually, in this age of authentic instruments, had a flared bell made for his English horn to use in performances of older music. Seeing the bells being changed in rehearsal, a conductor stopped and asked: "What's the difference?" to which came the answer: "Five guineas a concert."

Thomas Lot is also represented in *The Look of Music* by Nos. 68 and 72.

Boxwood, with ivory mounts. Three brass keys. H 80.0 cm. Institute of Theatre, Music and Cinematography, Leningrad, 524.

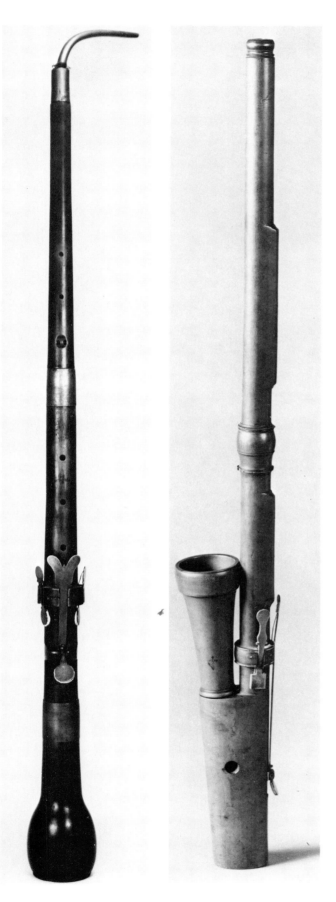

95. TENOR OBOE (Military model)

Jean-Hyacinth-Joseph Rottenburgh, Brussels (1672-1765)

This style of tenor oboe seems to have been made in considerable quantity for 18th century army bands, which actually consisted of no more than eight to twelve players as a rule. It was obviously a strictly functional design, perhaps slightly thicker in the lower joint, completely free of decorative turning which might get chipped away through rough use, and strengthened at the sockets not by a raised swelling in the wood but by sturdy brass bands. As all woodwinds were made by hand anyway, it would seem doubtful that any major reduction in the selling price would have been achieved by these economies, but that may be an erroneous assumption.

Wood undetermined, with brass mounts and three brass keys. In F. H 72.6 cm. Bate Collection, Oxford, 248.

96. BASS OBOE

Charles Bizey, Paris (. . .1716-1752. . .)

This instrument is perhaps the earliest, true bass oboe known today. The confusing use of "baritone" and "bass" in reference to such instruments, along with the existence of that strange *basse de musette* seen in many collections and the eventual Heckelphone (No. 240) make a very complex picture, which Philip Bate sorts out with his usual clarity and precision in the third edition of *The Oboe*. At any rate, this is one of the more interesting and, I would even say, delightful, shapes in this entire exhibition. It obviously has borrowed some features from the bassoon (it has the double-bored "boot joint" and not one but two wings), and its basic idea is reflected in later instruments of the oboe family in this exhibition, Nos. 235 and 239. On this instrument, however, and no other known to me, the upturned bell rises between the player and the instrument, rather than on the side away from the player. This is made necessary by the position of the long C key on the side of the boot joint away from the player.

Maple or boxwood, unmounted. Two brass keys and brass crook. H 81.75 cm. Musée Instrumental du Conservatoire de Paris, E.642, C.494.

98. CHALUMEAU IN C

Klenig   (German?)

Four *chalumeaux* as defined under No. 52 are preserved in Stockholm, a pair each by one Klenig and one Liebav. The former is known by only two other woodwinds and the latter by one. All four Stockholm *chalumeaux* seem to be immediate developments from J.C. Denner's prototype, the pear-shaped barrel being the more obvious difference. All four would seem to pre-date any known clarinet by Jakob Denner. (See No. 79).

Boxwood, unmounted, in three sections (mouthpiece and barrel a single section and a replacement bell, copied from the mate). Two brass keys covering diametrically opposed holes. H 49.0 cm. Bore, top of main section 1.32 cm. bottom of main section 1.22 cm. (The mate to this has precisely the same taper.) Musik Museet, Stockholm, 142.

99. IVORY CLARINET IN D

I. Scherer, Paris (?) (. . .1730-1764. . .)

Here is an early clarinet executed in ivory by this important Parisian maker, whose name suggests German origin. Its two keys and four sections make it almost certainly contemporary with the Jakob Denner clarinet (No. 79) and somewhat earlier, therefore, than the earliest working date often ascribed to Scherer. Very few ivory clarinets exist, while ivory flutes are comparatively common.

Ivory, unmounted, with two silver keys. Four sections, there being separate upper and lower joints; the mouthpiece and barrel are still integral. H 54.0 cm. Bore 1.3 cm. Musée Instrumental du Conservatoire de Paris, E.697, C.529.

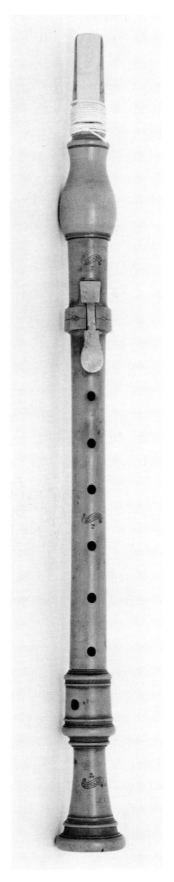

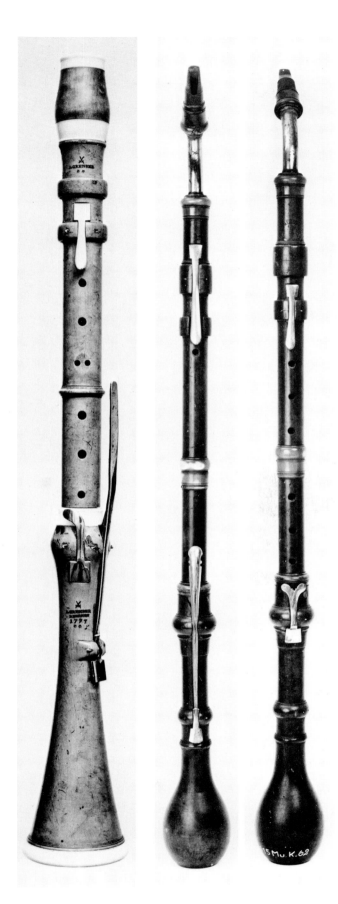

101. CLARINET IN C

August Grenser, Dresden (1720-1807)

Dated 1777

This is the earliest dated woodwind in *The Look of Music* but for the dated brass bell of the Eichentopf oboe *da caccia* (No. 83). This is astonishing, considering the fair consistency with which keyboards, strings, and even brasses were dated beginning in the 16th century. Johann Poerschman (Nos. 82, 84 and 85) did not date his instruments, to judge by the seven known to us, but both his celebrated apprentices did, August Grenser quite frequently and Jakob Grundmann consistently.

August Grenser, uncle of the equally important Heinrich, would seem to have been the earliest of an unbroken succession of much admired woodwind makers in Dresden that continued for over a hundred years. The two Grensers were responsible for the famed "Dresdener bassoon" that became among the more widely used on the continent, but they also both made flutes and oboes that survive in greater number than any of their other products but bassoons.

This four-keyed clarinet illustrates the addition of the g# key for right little finger, both it and the third key for e being mounted on the long bell. The next step (No. 178) would be the division of the long middle section in two, forming the upper and lower joints of today's instrument, on the lower of which these keys and the fifth key for f# would be mounted, rather than on the bell as here.

Boxwood, with ivory mounts. Four brass keys. Four sections, mouthpiece and barrel being separate parts. Finger holes 3 and 7 double. H 57.1 cm. without mouthpiece, which is missing. Musikinstrumenten-Museum der Karl-Marx-Universität, Leipzig, 1472.

102. CLARINET D'AMOUR

I.ST.W. (believed to be Johann Stefan Walch, Berchtesgaden

First half 18th century

A number of instruments stamped with these initials are known, and the fact that one is a three-keyed oboe and another a three-keyed clarinet indicate a working period within the time specified above, certainly not later. A Baroque-type rackett is also known. As discussed under No. 62, various Walchs made woodwinds in the Berchtesgaden area for more than 200 years, with a particular fondness for the clarinet family.

The French designation, *clarinet d'amour,* is the more common for this instrument vs. the Italian label *d'amore* for the alto oboe. Both woodwinds are supposedly an attempt to imitate the ethereal sound of the then-popular *viola d'amore* (Nos. 147 and 148), and both used a bulb-shaped bell to achieve a veiled if not particularly ethereal quality.

Maple, with horn mounts. Four brass keys. H 85.3 cm. Bayerisches Nationalmuseum, Munich, Mu 115.

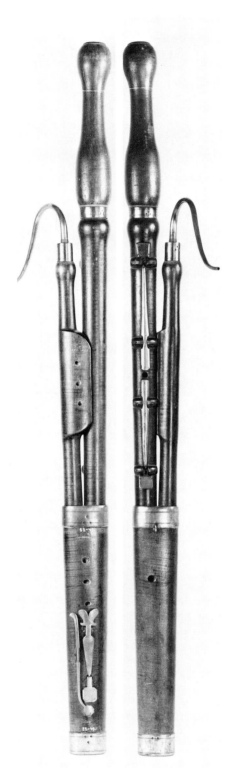

103. BASSOON

Johann Wolfgang Kenigsperger, Roding (?) (- 1752)

This is so unusual a bassoon profile that it might be viewed with suspicion but for the fact that there is another bassoon by Kenigsperger very much like it in the Germanisches National-musuem, Nürnberg. A third Kenigsperger bassoon is in Halle but has not been compared. The most striking feature is the bulbous bell, but the upper ends of the wing and bass joints are no less curious with their swollen bulges that are accentuated by the constriction of the adjacent brass bands, suggesting a fat man with too tight a belt. The final bulb of the bell is actually hollowed out slightly to form a *d'amore*-like chamber, below which is a slight "choke" in the bore diameter. In my opinion, no useful purpose is served by inventing a label *bassoon d'amore* to identify instruments with that feature, although Herbert Heyde has done so in reference to a bassoon and a *fagottino* in Eisenach.

The fourth key is a later addition.

Maple, with brass mounts and four brass keys. H 113.9 cm. Städt. Musikinstrumentensamm-lung, Munich, 52/49.

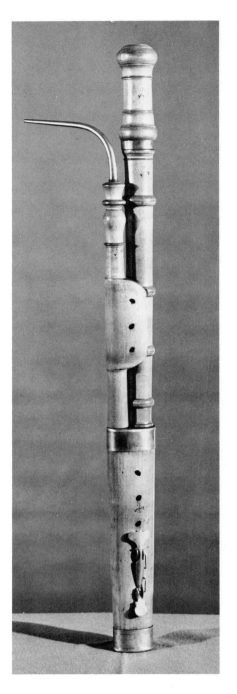

104. FAGOTTINO

I. Kraus

First half 18th century

Small bassoons are discussed under No. 49, and those general remarks pertain here as well. This is a handsome example that shows (by now familiar) Baroque characteristics and skilled workmanship. The I. Kraus stamp is one of the least legible in existence and more than once has been reported to read "C. Kraus" or to have a different first initial. The dozen examples I have been able to study are all "I. Kraus", and I must question the existence of any other 18th century maker of that surname, the conflicting readings of several experts notwithstanding.

Maple, with brass mounts and crook. Three brass keys. H 79.5 cm. Collection of Musical Instruments of Dorothy and Robert Rosenbaum, Scarsdale, 104.

105. RACKETT

W. Wyne, Nymwegen

circa 1700

This must be the best known rackett in existence, at least of the Baroque type, not only because of the frequency with which it has been illustrated but because it was the model for Otto Steinkopf's reproduction now made by Moeck and found today, in all likelihood, all over the world. The remarkable view looking through its parallel tubes has not been widely published but should be. The principle of the rackett (in whichever model) is explained under No. 10. The present example has brass bushings projecting from certain holes to permit them to be closed by the lower part of the fingers.

Boxwood, with brass mounts and crook. Body (only) H 21.0 cm. D 11.0 cm. Musikinstrumenten-Museum des Staatlichen Instituts f. Musikforschung-Preussischer Kulturbesitz, Berlin, 64.

106. RACKETT

Charles Bizey, Paris (. . .1716-1752. . .)

This rackett was believed to be without a maker's name until very recently. It has now been restored by the eminent Rainer Weber, who made the replacement bell and crook. It is obviously very similar to No. 105, but is covered with black leather on which there is considerable tooling in gold of heraldic lilies within a decorative border at the edges of the cylinder. There are three brass keys which seem very likely to be original. Ten parallel borings comprise the tube within the cylinder.

Maple, covered with black leather. Brass crook and three brass keys. Body (only) H 20.3 cm. D 9.0 cm. Bayerisches Nationalmuseum, Munich Mu 126.

107. WALDHORN IN F

Hieronymous Starck, Nürnberg (1640-1693)

Dated 1667

Waldhorn means "forest horn", therefore a hunting horn, even though the latter can also be specified as a *jagdhorn*. This relatively small, one-coil horn is among the earliest of this sort in existence, a predecessor of the instrument with wider diameter bell that would make its way into the salon and concert hall. All horns have a conical bore (derived from animal horns used for early instruments) vs. the mainly cylindrical bore of all trumpets, even those coiled in horn fashion. The present example is made in three separate, tapering sections. Baines says the instrument *"sounds easily up to its twelfth harmonic with a faintly bugle-like tone."* The coil is too small in diameter to go around the body, so would be held aloft to one side. It is an octave higher than the standard horn in f.

Brass Coil D 36.1 cm., bell D 10.9 cm. Tube length ca 176.0 cm. Musikhistorisk Museet og Carl Claudius' Samling, Copenhagen, F-99.

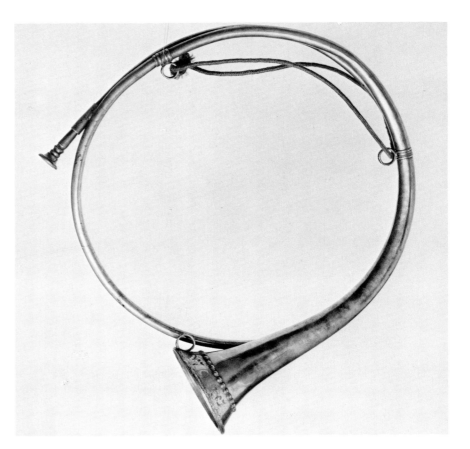

108. WALDHORN IN G

Friedrich Ehe, Nürnberg (1669-1743)

Another member of the celebrated Nürnberg brass-making family, Friedrich is represented by a number of trumpets, trombones, and horns in major museum collections. Although many are dated, this one is not. Bessaraboff, the brilliant cataloguer of this Boston collection, found it a superior instrument, giving the pedal tone GG without much effort. In his words, "the difference in the quality of tone between the open and stopped tones is not so considerable as on modern instruments."

Complete bell instription: *MACHT. FRIEDRICH EHE IN NUR.BG.*

Brass Coil D 41.0 cm., bell D 22.3cm., overall length of air column including replacement mouthpiece 350.0 cm. Museum of Fine Arts, Boston, 17.1999.

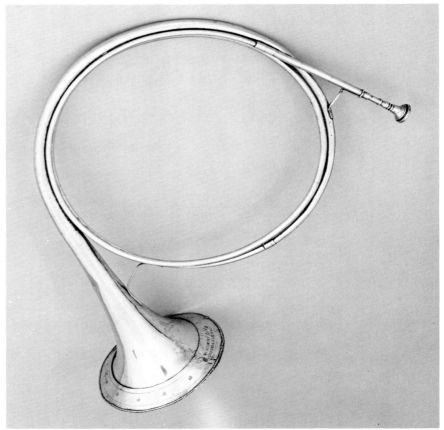

100

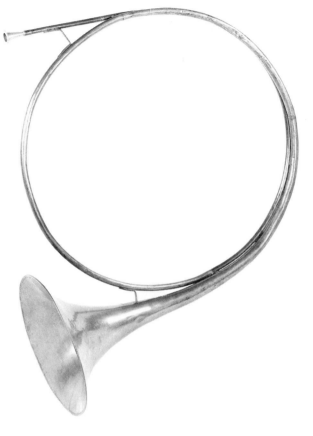

109. WALDHORN IN G (?)

Michael Saurle, Munich (ca 1796-ca 1861)

This instrument was made in the early 19th century but is of a type used earlier, very important in the development of the orchestral horn. It too, like No. 107, is a one-coil model, but the bell is larger, on the way toward the hand horn, in which the main coil would consist of two and a half full turns and the bell made large enough (and close enough, which it is not here) to permit use of the cupped hand inside the bell. No. 197 is an example of the type of instrument which developed from the waldhorn.

Complete bell inscription: *Michael Saurle in München*

Brass Coil D 56.0cm., bell D 28.3 cm. Stadt. Musikinstrumentensammlung, Munich, 41/64.

110. NATURAL HORN

Daniel Kodisch, Nürnberg (1686-1747)

The Germanisches Nationalmuseum guidebook calls this a "natural hunting horn", I think in order to avoid any implication that hand-stopping would have been used with such an instrument. It is a three-coil horn and therefore very close to the horn that was adopted for indoor use. This is the only known instrument by Daniel Kodisch, whose father-in-law was Michael Hainlein of the important brass-making family.

Complete bell inscription: MACH DANIEL KODISCH IN NÜRNBERG

Brass coil dia. ca 41.0 cm. Bell dia. ca 24.0 cm. Rück Collection, Germanisches Nationalmuseum, Nürnberg, MIR 76.

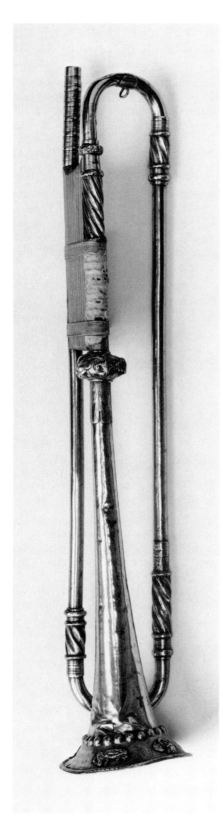

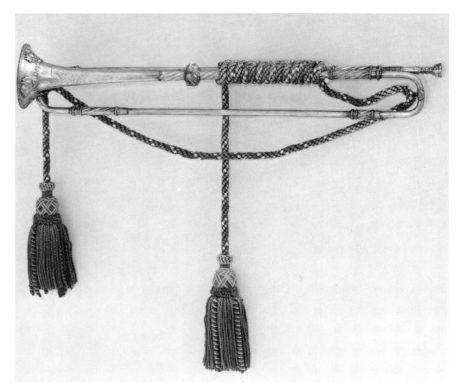

111. NATURAL TRUMPET

Hanns Geyer, Vienna (. . .1671-1698)

Dated 1684

Even with damaged bell, this is a lovely instrument. Its wooden block is here exposed to view, whereas on most other natural trumpets, the block and the portions of tubing that it braces are wound with a silk cord. Such trumpets need more stabilization than would be provided by the soldered joints of straight tubing fitted to the two U-bends, so the wrapped wood block near the upper end and a simple ring that links the bell rim and the adjacent U-bend give the necessary stability. The cross braces and stays found on early trombones are not used on these trumpets.

Brass L 57.0 cm. Bell dia. ca. 10.5 cm. Musik-historisk Museum og Carl Claudius' Samling, Copenhagen, F.88.

112. NATURAL TRUMPET IN Eb

Johann Wilhelm Haas, Numberg (1648-1723)

circa 1700

It is not extravagant to say that members of this family are the most famous trumpet makers of all time, and that Johann Wilhelm, the founder and father-grandfather, is the most celebrated of all. *The Look of Music* includes two of his instruments but none by his successors. See No. 113 for the significance of their trademarks.

This particular instrument is of silver, with more ornamentation than Haas often used, so in all probability it was made expressly for court use. Its centre knob or "boss" is washed with gold, and there is also a crest which may be that of the King of Saxony.

Silver. The mouthpiece is a copy of a Haas mouthpiece on another trumpet. L 71.2 cm. Bell dia. 11.7 cm. Metropolitan Museum of Art, New York, 54.32.1.

113. NATURAL TRUMPET

Johann Wilhelm Haas, Nürnberg (1649-1723)

circa 1700

The eminent brass historian, Don L. Smithers, was the first organologist to point out the significance of the Haas name and trademarks found on the garland of their instruments. All instruments bear the founder-father-grandfather's name with occasional slight variations: MACHT IOHANN WILHELM HAAS IN NÜRNBERG, for example. As a trademark, Johann Wilhelm uses a drawing of a hare (a pun on the German word for hare, *hase*) looking straight ahead (to the left) with the bold initials IWH above his body. His son and grandson, Wolf Wilhelm Haas and Ernst Johann Conrad Haas, use two other versions, each with the hare now looking back at the IWH initials, a symbol of indebtedness to their father-grand-father. Only the actual drawing of the hare reveals which son is the maker of the instrument. Wolf Wilhelm's hare's hind legs are pulled under his body, while Ernst Conrad's hare is in the midst of a long leap and the hind legs are flung straight out behind. Dr. Smithers' detailed account is in Volume XVIII of the Galpin Society *Journal,* but this summary is hoped to be of sufficient general interest to be worth inclusion here.

L 72.6 cm. with mouthpiece, Bell dia. 11.2 cm. Rück Collection, Germanisches Nationalmuseum, Nürnberg, MIR 106.

114. NATURAL TRUMPET

Michael Leichamschneider, Vienna (. . .1704-1741)

Dated 1725

In general, Viennese trumpets tend to be more ornate than most others, and Michael Leichamschneider's instruments are often especially beautiful. Leichamschneider is also an important figure in the development of the horn, apparently being the inventor of alternate crooks, used not only until the invention of valves but frequently preferred to valves well into this century.

Brass L 73.9 cm. including mouthpiece, bell 11.4 cm. Germanisches Nationalmuseum, Nürnberg, MIR 114.

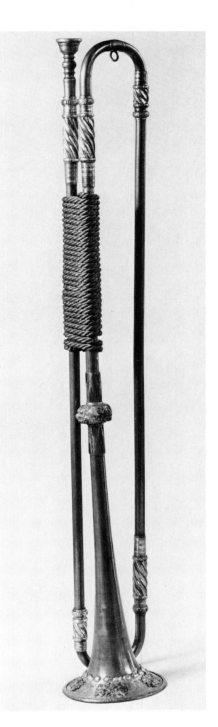

115. SOPRANO TROMBONE IN Bb

Johann Joseph Schmied, Pfaffendorf (...1748-1784...)

Dated 1781

In his monumental catalogue of the instruments in Boston's Museum of Fine Arts, Nicholas Bessaraboff makes a number of provocative points in discussing this particular instrument. He claims that our modern trumpet in Bb is not really a true, traditional trumpet at all, but a soprano trombone, equipped with valves. Bessaraboff explains how poorly the traditional slide works on a soprano instrument such as this, because the needed pitches are so close together along the slide, making it easier to overshoot them than on, say, a tenor or bass trombone. He insists that this instrument, if played with a trumpet mouthpiece, sounds exactly like the modern Bb trumpet (and sounds much better than when played with a soprano, trombone-shaped mouthpiece!) In short, he believes that we long ago let the "real" trumpet (the natural trumpet as used in the Baroque Period) be replaced by a soprano valve trombone, and that today's orchestras and bands are missing what could be a gorgeous additional voice, the true trumpet.

Soprano trombones are quite rare and have never attracted much use, but they appeared in the 17th century for a trial period, which is why this slightly later example is exhibited among Baroque instruments.

Complete bell inscription: IOHANN IOSEPH SCHMIED MACHTS IN PFAFFENDORF 1781

Brass L. 51.5 cm. Bell D 10.3 cm. Bore D 1.05 cm. L of air column with mouthpiece 134.5 cm. Museum of Fine Arts, Boston, 17.2006.

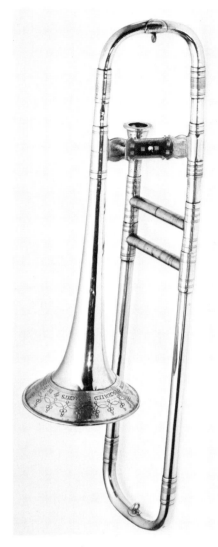

116. ALTO TROMBONE

Friedrich Ehe, Nürnberg (1669-1743)

This size of trombone is more successful and therefore has found more use than its soprano counterpart, No. 115. Altos are first mentioned in the late Renaissance, but they are quite rare today, partly because of the upward extension of the tenor's range through the influence of outstanding jazz trombonists. Even so, many principal trombonists in symphony orchestras are glad to have an alto available for Ravel's *Bolero* and similar, exposed sorties into outer space.

Overall L 149 cm. Bell dia. 12.4 cm. Germanisches Nationalmuseum, Nürnberg, MI 171.

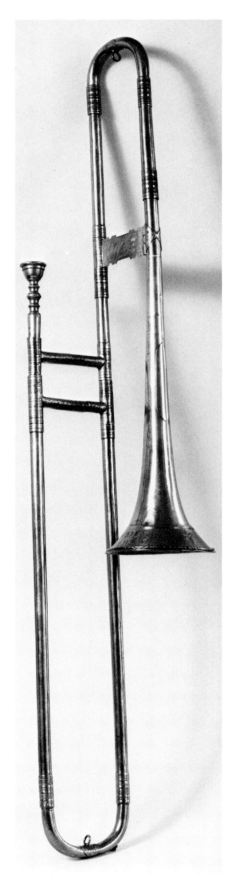

117. HURDY GURDY

Cloteaux, France

18th century (?)

The hurdy gurdy or *organistrum* is a very old and very important instrument, not to be confused with the hand-cranked mechanical music box associated with organ-grinders and monkeys with tin cups. The hurdy gurdy is first mentioned in a treatise dated 942 and is first depicted in the 12th century. At that time it was so long that it was held across the laps of two players, one cranking and one operating crude keys. The instrument consists of a sound box that may be copied after a fiddle, lute, or guitar, at the lower end of which is a wooden wheel with heavily rosined edge, over which the several strings pass, all sounding steadily as the wheel is cranked. Toward the upper end, near whatever neck there may be, is a box which houses the stopping devices that press down on the strings at appropriate places determined by a simple keyboard that projects from the box.

The instrument has enjoyed many spurts of popularity and fallow periods between. At one point it was the instrument

of beggars, at another, from which all four instruments in *The Look of Music* can be dated, it was a plaything of fashionable society. The French Revolution ended that.

This particular example has a guitar-shaped body with a carved female head above its pegbox. There are two melody strings *(chanterelles)* and two drone strings on either side, the separate bridges of which are missing here.

L 61.0 cm. Royal Ontario Museum, Toronto, 913.4.73.

118. HURDY GURDY

Anonymous, French

Late 18th century

It is believed that the overall body contour and the head-gear, a grenadier's cap, worn by the soldier atop the peg box, indicate a probable date at the end of the 18th century for this fine specimen. It also has two *chanterelle* strings that run through its key box and two drone strings on either side.

L 64.15 cm. Royal Ontario Museum, Toronto, 913.4.74.

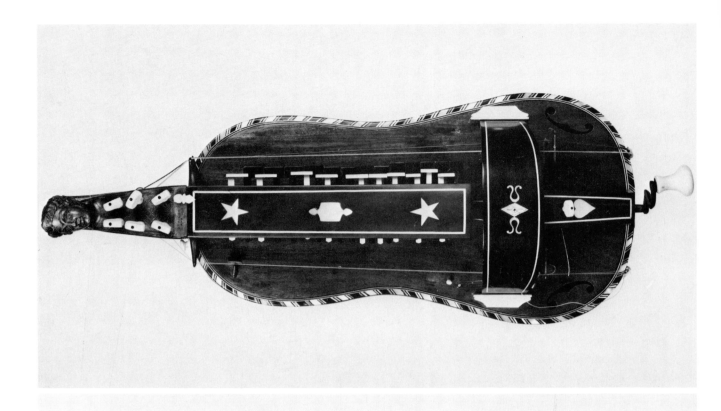

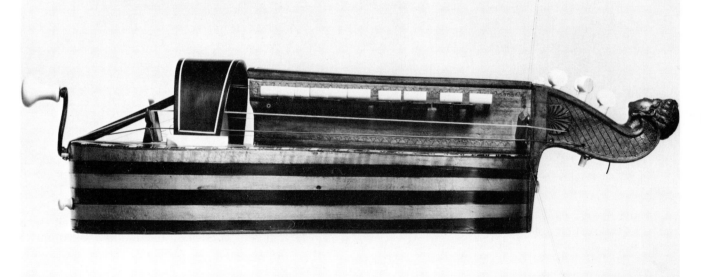

119. HURDY GURDY

Pierre Louvet, Paris (1711-1784)

Dated 1747

Louvet is one of the more important makers of hurdy gurdies, although he made many other types of instrument as well, even such diverse designs as harps and dulcimers. He is remembered particularly because he was made a *maitre luthier* at the age of twenty-five, a remarkable achievement. He is also credited with expanding the hurdy gurdy keyboard and developing advanced manufacturing techniques for this instrument. The present example has a body made of alternate strips of rosewood and maple, ivory and ebony stops, six ivory tuning pegs and ivory handle. The label inside reads: *Faite par Pierre Louvet, rue Montmartre, a la Vielle royale. Paris 1747, juin.* In addition, "P. Louvet" is stamped in several places on the exterior.

Overall L 67.0 cm. Musée Instrumental du Conservatoire de Paris, E.2056

106

121. LUTE

Joachim Tielke, Hamburg (1641-1719)

Dated 1696

This illustrious maker has just been accorded a degree of recognition until now reserved for Antonio Stradivari and very few other instrument makers of any century or specialization: he and his instruments are the subject of a book. The author is the celebrated Günther Hellwig, one of the major lute makers of our time and a pioneer of lute performance in this century. It is an extraordinarily beautiful book of photographs as well as an example of first-class scholarship. This lute is listed as No. 76.

Tielke is both an artist-maker of superb-sounding and playing instruments - lutes, viols, guitars, citterns, violins, and *violas d'amore,* in particular - and also one of the

supreme masters of instrument decoration, blessed with a gift for inlay, intarsia, woodcarving, and other forms of ornamentation. There is rarely any mistaking a Tielke instrument.

This lute has a spruce belly edged in ivory, an ebony bridge, and a body formed of nine flaming-maple ribs with reddish-brown varnish. There are ivory buttons at either end for a shoulder strap. The neck has intarsia of ivory which portrays Venus and Amor with a book resting on a pillar, between two floral designs. Engraved in black on the background are a chariot and other devices. Under the pillar is the inscription: *Amour ne peut/mal faire.* The fingerboard is of tortoiseshell, the pegs of ebony with ivory buttons. The pegbox is maple with ivory inlay. Label: *IOACHIM TIELKE/in Hamburg An. 1696.*

Overall H 80.0 cm. Body L 50.0 cm. Body W 30.6 cm. Body depth ca 16.0 cm. Dia. of rose 8.0 cm. Germanisches Nationalmuseum, Nürnberg, MI 349.

123. THEORBO-LUTE

Jacobus Anellus de Boctis

Dated 1674

The *theorbo* is described under No. 88, but that instrument has a considerably longer neck than this one. This is considered a theorbo-lute because it has a separate pegbox for bass strings that lie off the fingerboard, while having a standard-length lute neck and main pegbox bent backward at nearly a right angle. Many differing guesses are possible as to what is and is not original here. My own inclination is to believe that both pegboxes were added at a later time to an older lute. The label pasted inside reads as above, and may very well have been added also. Anellus is not listed in several of the standard guides. For all that, it is a handsome instrument.

Overall L 91.4 cm. 6 double courses and 8 bourdon. Royal Ontario Museum, Toronto, 913.4.49.

 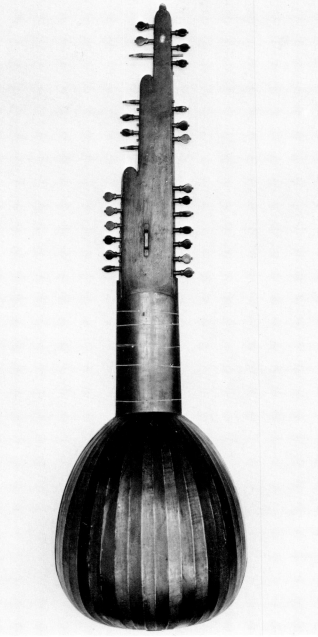

124. THEORBO

Matteo Sellas, Venice (. . .1600-1639. . .)

This instrument by an important, much admired maker has been frequently illustrated and discussed, and by now has a considerable array of testimonials to its ugliness! Michael Lowe has written that it "must be a strong contender for the title of the most unattractive lute ever made". Baines describes it as "a not so pretty model with three heads".

No-one reports how well or not so well it sounds, if indeed it is still playable, and of course until very recently there have not been very many theorboists to give an opinion. It is hard to imagine the light delicacy and grace that have always been associated with the lute coming from such a heavy, thick-set mass.

The body is made of twenty-one ribs. One single and six double courses are strung to the lowest pegbox, four double to the second, and three double to the highest, with string lengths 59.2 cm., 82.0 cm., and 100.8 cm. respectively.

Overall H 123.0 cm., body L 41.0 cm., body W 36.5 cm. The full tuning is given by Mahillon. Musée Instrumental, Brussels, 1565.

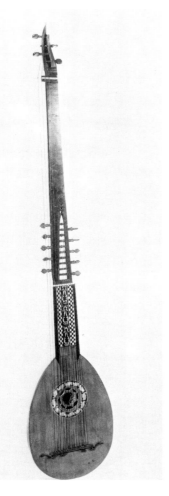

125. CHITARRONE

Damianian Zenarium, Venice

Dated 1662

The *chitarrone* is discussed under No. 25. It is doubtful that this specimen is an original *chitarrone;* instead, it is probably made from a lute body and neck. One authority whose advice I have sought believes it can only be the work of the notorious Leopoldo Franciolini of Florence, the most celebrated forger of the 19th century. Nevertheless, I consider it to be well worth inclusion in *The Look of Music.* (We can also learn from van Meergen's remarkable paintings in the style of Vermeer.)

L 152.4 cm. Five double courses to main pegbox, four single courses to upper. Royal Ontario Museum, Toronto, 913.4.47

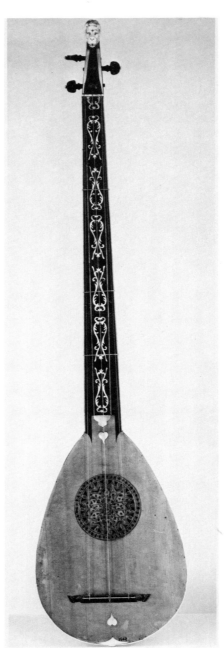

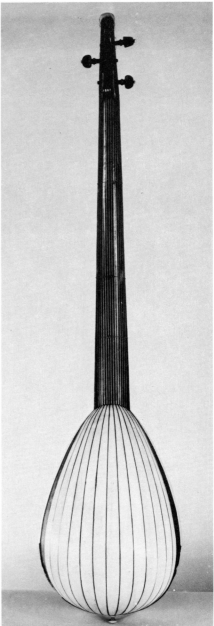

126. COLASCIONE

Anonymous, Italian

17th century

The *colascione* is a long-necked lute with disproportionately small body and usually only three strings, very much like the Near-Eastern model from which it derived. This one is superbly decorated with an ivory dog's head above the pegbox and tortoise-shell around the edges of the body. The body itself is made of ivory ribs interlaced with thin ebony strips. The fingerboard is ebony encrusted with ivory. The *colascione* is wire-strung, unlike the lute, and is played with a plectrum. It is still used today in Arabia, Turkey, Greece, and Yugoslavia, among other places.

Overall L 94.0 cm. Neck L 62.0 cm. Maximum body W 22.0 cm. Musée Instrumental, Brussels, 1567.

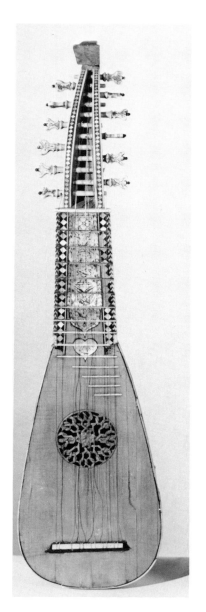

127. MANDORA

Benedetto Sanbretto, Roma

Dated 1726

The *mandora* is a type of small lute with a pegbox arching back over itself as here. Mandoras apparently existed in the Middle Ages and were made at least until 1800. This beautiful example is strung in six double courses. Ivory frets are set into the fingerboard and continue on to the belly; the bridge is faced with ivory, and the handsome pegs are incised ivory. Mother-of-pearl as well as ivory are used in other surface ornamentation.

H 56.5 cm. Royal Ontario Museum, Toronto, 908.13.2

128. MANDOLA

Gaetano Vinaccia, Naples

Dated 1744

The Vinaccia name is particularly associated with the mandolin, at first an Italian folk instrument and then used frequently in the concert hall and opera pit as well. The term *mandola* was initially a synonym for *mandora* but became by the time of this present instrument the term for a large, early mandolin.

This instrument has only four double courses of wire strings, the lower two overspun to deepen their pitch. The body is comprised of 24 rosewood ribs. The protective plate on the belly is of tortoiseshell. The Gaetano who made this instrument may be one of the earlier members of this celebrated family; there is another maker by this name with the dates 1779-1821, according to Lütgendorf. Antonio is the most famous of all.

Overall L 108.0 cm. Body L 53.0 cm. Body maximum W 33.0 cm. String length 77.5 cm. Musée Instrumental, Brussels, 3182.

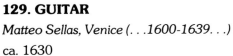

129. GUITAR

Matteo Sellas, Venice (. . .1600-1639. . .)

ca. 1630

Old and young alike may be comforted by the fact that guitar-like instruments dating from between the fourth and eighth centuries have been excavated in Egypt. In Europe the earliest references date from the 14th century, and in the 15th the guitar-like *vihuela* was becoming established in Spain, as an instrument which could be both plucked and bowed. Very few guitars exist of earlier date than the present specimen, and very few are more beautiful. Its vaulted back is of rosewood strips separated by ivory fillets, which are carried over to the ribs as well. The rose is of gilded lead, broadly edged in ivory and ebony. The fingerboard has panels of ivory on which are engraved scenes from *Aesop's Fables.* There are five double courses of strings. The frets are the tied-on sort also used on the lute.

Overall L 87.0 cm. Maximum W 26.0 cm. Musée Instrumental, Brussels, 550.

130. GUITAR

Joachim Tielke, Hamburg (1641-1719)

Dated 1687

The importance of this maker was discussed under No. 121. Most fortunately *The Look of Music* includes four instruments by this master, all from Europe.

The decoration on this instrument is quite exceptional, even for Tielke, from the ivory-edged pegbox with ivory pegs to the extraordinary inlaid-ivory flowers on the back, ribs, neck and fingerboard. The belly is made from an especially beautiful single piece of spruce.

There are ivory plugs set into the pegbox to fill holes left by the other four pegs that were there originally. These five double courses might have been tuned A - d - g - b - e'. When reduced to six single courses, probably in the 18th century, the tuning would have been the same as on modern guitars.

This guitar is No. 42 in G. Hellwig's book on J. Tielke, listed in the bibliography.

Overall L 92.5 cm. Body L 44.2 cm. Body widths 19.9 cm., 18.0 cm. and 23.9 cm. Ribs H 7.0-9.8 cm. Musikhistorisk Museum og Carl Claudius' Samling, Copenhagen, C 83.

131. PANDORA

Anonymous, Italian?

17th century (?)

This instrument represents an enigma about which there has been considerable speculation and scepticism. Anthony Baines summarizes the situation: "A number of collections possess examples of a curious type of instrument, rather heavily built but with a three-lobed body with some ten courses of strings (generally gut) tied to a bridge in the lute manner . . . Against the conclusion that all these specimens may be of some 18th century variety of instrument, it should in fairness be added that the example formerly in the Galpin Collection . . . was found to contain 16th century Italian printed paper in its linings."

This Toronto specimen has seven double courses. It does not seem to have been pointed out elsewhere that a number of instruments of this type and body outline have a rose in which is incorporated the Star of David. Other types of instrument also exhibit this symbol, but not, I have observed, with the frequency of this one.

H 160.3 cm. Royal Ontario Museum, Toronto, 913.4.45.

132. VIOLIN, THREE QUARTER SIZE

Antonio Stradivari, Cremona (1644-1737)

Dated 1736

The Look of Music displays very few members of the violin family. The reason is that almost all fine specimens — whether violins, violas, celli, or double basses — are in daily use, today as much as one hundred years ago, two hundred years ago, and likely three hundred years ago. No performer can part with his instrument for six months. Relatively few great violins are in museums.

This three-quarter size violin is by the acknowledged master of masters. Many of the best-known players actually prefer an instrument made by one of the Guarneri family or one of the Amati, each of which has certain qualities that distinguish it from one of the other Cremona makers' instruments, which in turn have their particular strengths, as well. It is touching that, when affixing his printed label to the inside of this instrument, the old man proudly added in his own handwriting, "From his 92nd year."

Overall L. 56.52 cm. Body widths 15.24 cm., 10.24 cm. and 19.05 cm. Body L. approximately 33.81 cm. Body D. 5.86 cm. Yale University, Collection of Musical Instruments, New Haven, 281.

133. VIOLIN

Antonio Stradivari, Cremona (1644-1737)

Dated 1724

This instrument belonged to Pablo Sarasate (1844-1908), the great Spanish virtuoso. He was accepted as a student at the Paris Conservatoire when 12 years old, and it is there in the Musée Instrumental du Conservatoire that this violin normally resides today. The instrument was actually presented to him as a boy by Queen Isabella of Spain, and he used it throughout his career. A successful copy of it was made for him by Vuillaume (Nos. 296 and 297) and was sometimes used by Sarasate at rehearsals.

Of this particular instrument, the Brothers Hill in their standard book on Antonio Stradivari have this to say: "There still remain to us some fine examples of 1721 and the following years, which, if not comparable with those of the preceding decade as regards beauty of wood and varnish, are in no way inferior to them in point of form and construction; indeed, some of the finest-toned instruments date from these years. The violin invariably played upon in public by Senor Sarasate is of the year 1724. Though unattractive in appearance, it captivates all hearers by its tone."

Body L 35.7 cm. Body widths 17 cm., 11.5 cm., 20.5 cm. Musée Instrumental du Conservatoire de Paris, E.1729.

135. VIOLA MADE FROM A TENOR VIOL

Johann Ullrich Eberle, Prague (1699-1768)

Dated 1729

Eberle is an important Prague maker, a pupil of Thomas Edlinger II. This instrument was acquired by the Royal Ontario Museum in 1973 and appears to be the earliest known instrument by this maker. As happened so often to many of the better instruments as viols lost favour, this was converted to a viola, probably in the 19th century. The carved head, neck, fingerboard, bridge and tailpiece are all replacements. The ribs have been cut down in order to reduce the thickness of the body, with the result that the back is now flat without the sloping upper portion it had previously.

Overall L 72.5 cm. Body length 42.2 cm. Body widths 19.6 cm., 13.3 cm. and 24.8 cm. Ribs H 4.7 cm. Royal Ontario Museum, Toronto, 973.200.

134. VIOLIN

Jakob Stainer, Absom (1617-1683)

Dated 1661

During their lifetimes and for some time beyond, Jakob Stainer was better know than the Amatis or Stradivaris, and his violins were more highly regarded than theirs. In fact, the point is often made that Antonio Stradivari has only been regarded as *Numero Uno* since 1800, when brilliance of tone and large volume became the most important qualities sought in a violin. (This is explained more fully in the introduction to instruments of the Classic Period, page 139). Until then, Stainer and the several Amati were the preference of most violinists. Stainer instruments have deeply vaulted bellies and backs, which help to produce a sweeter, warmer tone. One can hear these qualities as much today as then.

In 1669, poor Stainer fell under suspicion of Lutheranism and was imprisoned and eventually forced to recant. He continued to make instruments at least until 1677, but his mind began to fail and he remained insane until his death. Among those who owned and played on Stainer violins were Locatelli, Veracini, Biber, Leopold Mozart, and Johann Sebastian Bach.

Spruce belly, maple ribs and back, ebony fingerboard and tailpiece. One-piece back. Original label most certainly dated 1656, with a later replacement label dated 1661. Overall L 58.34 cm. Body widths 16.27 cm. 10.52 cm. and 20.0 cm. Body depth 6.67 cm. Yale University, Collection of Musical Instruments, New Haven, 387.

136. VIOLA MADE FROM A VIOLA D'AMORE

Johann Joseph Elsler, Mainz (. . .1717-1750)

Dated 1746

This instrument will be listed as a large viola in *The Look of Music,* on the assumption that it began life as a *viola d'amore.* The Royal Ontario Museum catalogue labels it a small tenor viol, but the body is not the shape of a viol, either from the front or in depth. Belly and back overhang the ribs, and the fingerboard is too long for a viol. The presence of a fifth string does indeed make it an unusual viola, but of course such instruments exist. According to Jalovec, Elsler made violas as well as violins and viols. He is considered a follower of Stainer in terms of design.

L. 73.7 cm. Royal Ontario Museum, Toronto, 913.4.7.

137. VIOLONCELLO

Thomas Urquhart, London (1625-after 1680)

Dated 1659

Urquhart is an important early English luthier and is said to have been the teacher of Edward Pamphilon and Barak Norman (No. 143). The latter is better known and specialized in viols, while Urquhart seems to have made no viols whatever. Instead he made both violins and at least three celli, perhaps many more. Oddly enough, he also made flutes! His violins are on the model of Gasparo da Salo's and his celli must have been among the very first made in England.

The belly of his cello is made from a slab that has been cut rather than quarter-sawed, and has a flame grain rather than the usual straight grain. The ribs and back are both of maple, and the fingerboard and tailpiece are ebony.

Overall H 125.0 cm. Body widths 35.2 cm., 23.3 cm. and 42.8 cm. Depth ca. 20 cm. Yale University, Collection of Musical Instruments, New Haven, 434.

138. VIOLONCELLO

Martin Kaiser, Venice (1609?-1679)

Dated 1679

This interesting cello has its original neck with marks left behind by gut tied-on frets, a sign that the owner had started as a viol player and needed viol frets on the new instrument. In the back are two holes into the sound box which made it possible to suspend the cello from a sash around the neck, both for playing standing up and for marching.

Overall H 120.0 cm. Body H 71.5 cm. Body maximum width 46.0 cm. Body depth 13.0 cm. Fingerboard L 40.5 cm. Musée Instrumental, Brussels, 1441

139. DOUBLE BASS

Gasparo de Salo, Brescia (1540-1609)

instrument ca. 1600

This instrument, once owned by the double bass virtuoso Domenico Dragonetti (1763-1846), is attributed to Gasparo da Salo, one of the earliest makers of strings.

H 190.5 cm. Bow L 71.15 cm. Royal Ontario Museum, Toronto, 915.19.1

118

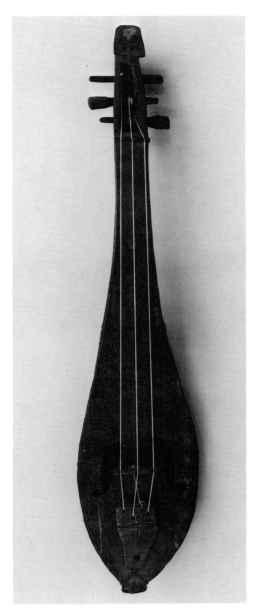

140. REBEC

Anonymous, Italian

17th century (?)

This specimen and its companion (No. 141) are folk instruments for casual playing and enjoyment, probably made in the 17th century, and show how little some types of instruments change through the centuries. These are one of the two or three direct forerunners of the violin. They are tuned in fifths, are bowed overhand, and are played on the shoulder: all characteristic of violins from their beginning, and in contrast to coexistent viols.

The pegbox, neck, fingerboard, and body are all carved from a single block of wood, with the belly attached separately after the body has been hollowed out and reduced on the exterior to a tear-drop shape. Three strings are tied over the bridge to a tailpiece in turn tied to an end pin.

There is a sound post. The sound is wiry and penetrating, two criticisms also expressed in reference to the early violin. It seems very possible that one of these two examples is a copy of the other.

L. 56.2 cm. Body W at bridge 11.8 cm. Private collection, Vancouver.

141. REBEC

Anonymous, Italian

18th century(?)

L 56.8 cm. Body W. at bridge 12.8 cm. Private collection, Vancouver

142. DISCANT VIOL

Würfl

17th century

This handsome instrument is by a maker of whom very little is known. The fingerboard is made of five tapering strips of two alternating, contrasting woods, an unusual and lovely effect which is carried onto the body as well, where both ribs and back are wide, alternating bands of the same woods. A lion's head is above the pegbox. The soundholes are of particular interest because their extremely nice contours are not connected to the small round holes adjacent to them, the so-called ''angels' heads'', as they usually are. Finally, the body outline itself is quite attractive with its double lower bouts creating a soundbox of usual length for its width at any point.

Overall H 75.0 cm. Body widths 18.3 cm., 13.1 cm., 21.7 cm. and 21.3 cm. Musikhistorisk Museum og Carl Claudius' Samling, Copenhagen, C261a.

143. BASS VIOL

Barak Norman, London (1678-1740)

Dated 1697

Here is one of the great English instrument makers of any age, although England was blessed with a number of outstanding viol makers at this particular time. I know of no evidence to suggest that Barak Norman's fondness for surface ornamentation was influenced by Tielke, but that thought will occur as one studies the detailed photographs here. Actually, Tielke worked much more in the black and white brilliance of ebony and ivory, while Norman dealt more often with contrasting woods, as here. The label inside the body reads: *Barak Norman at the Basse Viole in St. Paul's alley, London, Fecit 1697*. If that date is correct and has been accurately read, Norman was only 19 years old when he made this viol.

Overall H 114.3 cm. Royal Ontario Museum, Toronto, 913.4.30.

144. BASS VIOL

Joachim Tielke, Hamburg (1641-1719)

Dated 1698

This is an exceedingly handsome instrument in every way, the absence of Tielke's usual ornamentation notwithstanding. I find the plain simplicity very refreshing and also an aid in judging the basic proportions and lines of the instrument. The tailpiece, fingerboard, neck, and the pegs are all replacements. The pegbox decoration deserves special mention.

Tielke made more viols than any other instrument. Gunther Hellwig lists 71 compared with 14 lute types, 25 guitars, 5 violins, and 8 *violas d'amore*.

This bass viol is No. 90 in G. Hellwig's book on J. Tielke, listed in the bibliography.

Overall H 109.5 cm. Body H 59.0 cm. Body widths 27.2 cm., 20.0 cm., 33.5 cm. Ribs H at neck 11.5 cm. Musikhistorisk Museum og Carl Claudius Samling, Copenhagen, D 80.

145. BASS VIOL

Maria Valenziano, Padua

Dated 1767

The lone woman instrument maker in *The Look of Music* is this person of whom almost nothing seems to be known. Jalovec lists her as "a woman known to have made a bass viol" and adds that it was made in 1764, so perhaps there is another example of her work, present whereabouts unknown, as well as this. This viol has been converted to a cello, so it is very likely that only the body is original.

The printed label has her last name spelled with a "z", but for whatever reason it is spelled with a "c" in the books that mention her at all.

The only other woman involved with instrument making until modern times, I think, was Nannette Stein Streicher, the daughter of the important piano maker Johann Andreas Stein of Augsburg. She learned the craft from her father and, upon marriage to Johann Streicher, formed a partnership with her husband and her brother in Vienna.

Overall H (without cello and pin) 110.0 cm. Body H 68.0 cm. Body widths 31.0 cm. middle ?, 38.0 cm. body depth 11.5 cm. Museum für Hamburgische Geschichte, Hamburg, 1921.100.

146. BASS VIOL

Johann Ulrich von Läutter.

Dated 1770

Johann Ulrich von Läutter. . .in. . .fecit at anno 1770.
The partly illegible label is given as fully as possible here
because this maker is not in the standard books of luthiers.
The term *viola bastarda* is used by Praetorius writing in
1619 with very few details of what constitutes an instrument thus named, although he does say that sometimes in
England the *viola bastarda* has sympathetic strings. The
Royal Ontario Museum catalogue uses this designation for
the present instrument, which does not seem justified for a
specimen made 150 years later, in all likelihood in Southern Germany. This diagnosis is shared by others who have
seen the instrument. It would seem more appropriate to
describe it as a bass viol of attractive (but not unique)
profile rather than typical viol shape. It is a very pretty
instrument whatever it is called.

Overall H 123.2 cm. Royal Ontario Museum, Toronto, 913.4.32

124

147. VIOLA D'AMORE

Caspar Stadler, Munich (. . .1705-1735)

Dated 1714

The *viola d'amore* is an important 18th century instrument with normally six or seven gut strings bowed in the usual manner and with the same number or more wire strings lying below the bridge and under the fingerboard, in any case safely out of reach of the bow. These metal strings were tuned to vibrate in sympathy with the bowed gut strings, and were set in vibration by the sound waves coming from the gut strings. The combined timbre is somewhat ethereal and has a silvery resonance. This specimen is very well-known and certainly one of the more beautiful in existence. It is unusual for the original bow to

be preserved with a specific instrument, but in this case that has been done. It is designed and decorated in matching style, and is beautiful in its own right as well as heightening the beauty of its instrument. Emanuel Winternitz has proclaimed this set to be "an outstanding example of German 18th century design". The back and ribs are of rosewood with intarsia of silver and brass. At the top of the back are two wind instrumentalists, below which are a harpist and another musician with a shawm or trumpet, and lower still a lady tuning a cittern with a lute behind her, and another lady playing a viol. That is supposedly a dancing dog at the bottom!

Overall L 75.2 cm. L of body 37.7 cm. Body widths 18.6 cm. 12.7 cm. 23 cm. Germanisches Nationalmuseum, Nürnberg, MI 208.

148. VIOLA D'AMORE

Louis Guersan, Paris (ca.1713-ca.1781)

Dated 1761

This instrument has seven bowed and only six sympathetic strings, flame-shaped sound holes, and a blindfolded head of the god Amor atop the open pegbox. The flame sound holes and blindfolded Amor are usual on *violas d'amore,* and the latter may have contributed to the name of the instrument. It was in vague imitation of the *violas d'amore* that oboes in particular, but also clarinets and even flutes were made in *d'amore* or *d'amour* versions, usually slightly lower pitched and with a bulbous end-piece (Nos. 80 and 102, for example).

Complete label inscription: *Ludovicus Guersan Prope Comoediam Gallicam Lutetiae, Anno 1761.* ("near the Comédie Française")

H 71.1 cm. Royal Ontario Museum, Toronto, 923.28.

149. VIOLA POMPOSA

Anonymous

Late 18th century

The origin and function of the *viola pomposa* have been mentioned under No. 87. This present example is not nearly so deep-ribbed and therefore more typical. Dr. John Henry van der Meer has suggested that the date of this specimen may be as late as the beginning of the 19th century, pointing out that in Bohemia at least, *violas pomposa* were made until nearly the beginning of the 20th century. This instrument has traces of a label inside, but no maker's name is discernible.

Two-piece spruce belly, birdseye maple ribs and back, maple neck, ebony nut and tailpiece. Overall H 76.0 cm. Body H 43.0 cm. Bouts 24.0 cm. 16.3 cm. and 30.2 cm. Rück collection, Germanisches National-museum, Nürnberg, MIR 836

150. PARDESSUS DE VIOLE

Francois le Jeune, Paris (. . .1753-1789. . .)

Dated 1753

This splendid instrument is by one of the major Parisian luthiers of the time. Its proportions and workmanship are particularly fine. The pardessus is a soprano viol, therefore played upright on the knee, while a somewhat similar contemporary instrument, the quinton, is held on the shoulder or at the neck. Both instruments have five strings rather than the viol's usual six and the violin's invariable four. What makes the pardessus a true viol, however, is the knee position in which it is played, its tied-on frets, its tuning in fourths with the middle third, and the underhand grip with which its bow is held.

Spruce belly, maple ribs, neck, and back, ebony fingerboard. Overall H 66.8 cm. Body H 36.0 cm. Bouts 17.5 cm. 12.7 cm. and 20.5 cm. Musée Instrumental du Conservatoire de Paris, C.144, E.370.

 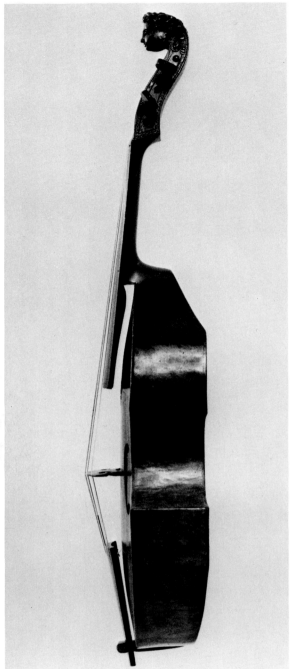

151. PARDESSUS DE VIOLE

Pierre Morant, Caen

Dated 1709

A few years ago a man appeared in a Vancouver music store, carrying an instrument in a paper bag which he offered for sale. This is the instrument, an extremely handsome one by a maker not listed in any of the standard books. It also has the unusual feature of a slanted lower panel on its back as well as the usual slanted upper panel.

Since first examining the instrument I have had opportunity to visit many major instrument collections and have yet to see another instrument so constructed. Dr. John Sawyer, of the Music Department of the University of British Columbia, a viol specialist, has suggested that this is in all likelihood an alteration to the original form, carried out in order to allow the instrument to be played on the shoulder, otherwise difficult because of (typical viol) body depth.

Overall H 63.6 cm. Bouts 17.5 cm. 12.5 cm. and 20.2 cm. depth 7.5 cm. Ward Music Ltd., Vancouver.

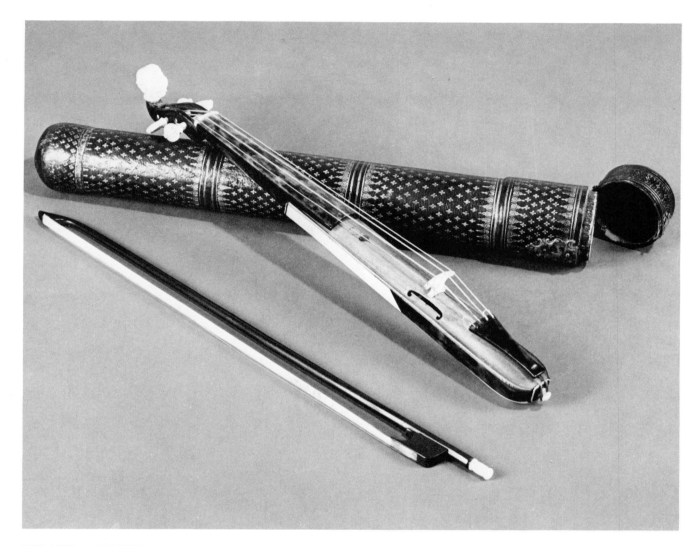

152. KIT or POCHE

Mathias Wörle, Augsburg (ca.1650?-ca.1695)

Dated 1668

The date on this label suggests that the rough birth date given in various books is not early enough. It seems unlikely that an 18-year-old would have the consummate skill to make such an exquisite instrument, bow, and case.

This design is known as a "dancing master's fiddle", as well as by the two names given above. It was made in such a compact, slim form because in a dance studio neither quality of tone nor volume were that important and an instrument of these proportions could be easily carried about by the violinist thus employed. The term *poche,* in fact, comes from the well-documented fact that, even without a protective case, a kit was routinely transported in a long pocket sewn into the tails of the violinist's tailcoat. This form of slim violin is actually very common and a favourite with instrument collectors. There are many widely contrasting body shapes employed but all use reduced body dimension.

Tortoise fingerboard and tail piece, back is alternate bands of ivory and tortoiseshell. Ivory pegs, carved head above pegbox, nut, and end button. Four gut strings, the lower wound with brass. Overall H 42.3 cm. Body W 3.54 cm. Collection of Musical Instruments of Dorothy and Robert Rosenbaum, Scarsdale, 274.

153. VIRGINAL

Ioannes Ruckers, Antwerp (1578-1643)

Dated 1622

Ruckers is the most revered name in the history of keyboard instruments. This statement is meant to take nothing from the contribution of Cristofori, or the marvellous sound — even today — of organs by Silbermann and Schnitger and the pianos of Stein, Graf, or Broadwood, but simply to recognize what continues to be the judgement of musicians today as much as 400 years ago. It would also seem true that we have learned more about the Ruckers family in the past 20 years than was learned in the previous two centuries.

Hans the Elder, founder of the dynasty, was survived by very few instruments that escaped later alteration. This virginal was made by his son Ioannes (Hans the Younger) who worked for a while in partnership with his younger brother Andreas (the Elder). The two brothers, both distinguished masters of the first rank, also worked independently of each other. A rose containing the maker's initials (here "IR") is a Ruckers characteristic, but too easily counterfeited to be proof of authenticity. So admired was the brilliance and clarity of tone of all Ruckers instruments that a great many — even most — were altered for 100 years and more afterward to increase their range and variety of tonal resources. In the opinion of one authority, this particular virginal is "about the most completely original, untouched Ruckers instrument in existence". It was formerly in the private collection of Victor Mahillon of Brussels (see No. 65).

Overall L 170.2, overall 49.4, overall H 26.0 cm. Compass now C-f''', originally C/E-c'''. No. 40 by this maker in Boalch, 2nd edition. Metropolitan Museum of Art, New York, 11.176.1.

154. SPINET

Anonymous, English

Late 17th-Early 18th century

The shape and overall form of this and the following instrument must be one of the most handsome ever devised. The bent side and its reflection in the contour of the top create a silhouette that is quite lovely from any perspective. This specimen may not have always been anonymous, for the name board (on which the maker's name traditionally appears) directly above the keys appears to be a replacement. Carved crudely in the surface of the top are the initials "IC". The details of the thrashing that surely resulted from this vandalism are mercifully not recorded.

Walnut, with brass hardware, ebony(?) naturals and very yellowed ivory accidentals, naturals with ivory arcaded fronts. Overall L 166.5 cm. overall D 62.2 cm, overall H with lid closed 82.5 cm. Compass AA-c'''. Montreal Museum of Fine Arts, 65.Df.6.

155. SPINET

Baker Harris, London (. . .1740-1780. . .)

Dated 1773

The English gift for apt terminology here results in what is widely understood to be a "leg of mutton" case. This instrument is more elegant than the bare walnut model just discussed but no more beautiful, in my opinion. Its maker is well known for his spinets and is survived by at least eighteen such instruments but only two harpsichords. He also made pianos and organs. The characteristics of a spinet are presented under No. 1. It is the simplest and most compact type of harpsichord and is intended for the home.

Overall L 186.7 cm. Compass FF-f'' No. 11 by this maker in Boalch, 2nd edition. Royal Ontario Museum, Toronto, 913.4.100.

156. CLAVICHORD

Hieronymous Albrecht Hass, Hamburg (1689-1744...?)

Dated 1744

The Hass family worked in Hamburg in the 18th century and were considered the finest German makers of harpsichords and clavichords. It is now believed that Hieronymous was the first of the family, followed by an illustrious son, Johann Adolph (No. 158). (They must not be confused with Johann Wilhelm Haas and sons, the celebrated trumpet makers of Nürnberg.)

This attractive clavichord is of the unfretted variety that was developed after the fretted type and coexisted with it for much of the 18th century. The clavichord mechanism itself is the simplest imaginable and uses a brass blade called a "tangent" affixed to the inner end of the key, which lightly strikes a string when the key is depressed. The action is therefore a tapping rather than the plucking accomplished by various harpsichord types. On an unfretted clavichord there is a separate string (here, two or three strings) for each pitch of the compass, while the earlier, fretted model produced two or more pitches from many of its single strings, therefore having fewer strings and being more compact. The late Thurston Dart characterized the clavichord as "the best instrument other than the lute for expressing personal feelings of an agreeably melancholy kind". The scene on the underside of the lid is of Altona in 1746, around which are other engraved scenes and musicians playing various instruments.

Overall L 171.0 cm. overall 52.0 cm. Compass F-f‴. Musée Instrumental, Brussels, 2518.

157. HARPSICHORD

Michel Richard, Paris (. . .1659-1693?. . .)

Dated 1688

This instrument was long believed to be by Hans Ruckers because of its "HR" rose (see No.153), but it is now ascribed to this slightly later maker because of an inscrip-tion on the underside of the soundboard: "Faict par Michel Richard 1688". It is a splendid example of a two-manual 17th century harpsichord with three sets of strings, 2 of 8' length and one 4', the latter on the upper manual. The Yale description is a model of clarity and detail: "The case has a plywood replacement bottom. It and the lid, both inside and out, are painted black and decorated with Chinoiserie in gold, silver, and copper tones. The sound-board is painted with flowers; arabesques and scalloped

lines, painted in green, outline and bridges and nuts. The instrument rests on a gilded Louis XIV stand with seven turned and carved legs. . .The compass is four and one-half octaves, GG-c''', with split apparent EEb. The natural keys are of ebony with arcaded wooden fronts; the sharp keys are of wood with ivory veneer. The bridges are of walnut; the 8' bridge has a bent treble and a carved bass, the 4' bridge is bent. The walnut slides and the jacks, voiced in Delrin, are modern. There is no manual coupler.

There is a buff stop for the 8'. Two metal handstops protrude through either side of the nameboard: the right hand knob controls the buff stop, the left-hand knob controls the 4'. Another metal handstop on the wrestplank controls the back 8'.''

Overall L 194.3 cm. Overall W 82.6 cm. Yale University, Collection of Musical Instruments, New Haven, 473, on loan from The Museum of Art, Rhode Island School of Design.

159. FIELD SNARE DRUM

Anonymous, Würzburg

Dated 1724

Drums of this age and colourful appearance are now nearly all in museums, or ground into the battlefield long ago. To find one with its original sticks intact is very rare indeed. A drum of this design was for military or ceremonial use and would never have found its way into the concert hall. The rope lacing and leather tighteners survive today only on children's toys. There is a painted design on the drum shell, perhaps even a coat of arms, but it is too soiled and worn to be recognizable but for "Wurzburg" and the date. There is considerable feeling today among curators and organologists that not every specimen should be "restored": at least some should be preserved as they are, for future enthusiasts and scholars to enjoy in the worn state in which the instrument has come down to us.

Drum H 53.0 cm. dia. 53.0-55.0 cm. Sticks L 44.5 cm. wide end dia. 2.8 cm. tip dia. 2.22 cm. Collection of Musical Instruments of Dorothy and Robert Rosenbaum, Scarsdale, 331.333.

160. PAIR OF TIMPANI

Anonymous, English

Late 18th century

These are the typical timpani of Haydn's and Mozart's orchestra. The bowls are of copper, but rest on fixed wrought iron legs. One drum was equipped with seven tuning screws, the other with eight, and natural skin was used for the heads. Decorative zinc plates are embossed with Rococo motifs and form a plate at the base of each tuning screw.

936.20.1a dia. 55.0 cm. Bowl D 34.0 cm. 936.20.1b dia. 57.0 cm. Bowl D 34.0 cm. Royal Ontario Museum, Toronto, 936.20.1a, 936.20.1b.

161. THREE TIMPANI STICKS

Anonymous

Early 18th century

This nice set of three timpani sticks is of interest not only because of their antiquity but also as a reminder that padded tips were not always the norm. Until the late 18th century, timpani and kettledrums were used only to accompany trumpets, with which they had a traditional relationship; one was never used without the other. Modern mallet instrument players use four and more mallets at a time, and the reader may wonder why there are three sticks in this set. The third is simply a spare.

Each stick L 28.4 cm. Head 3.1 cm. Head is integral piece with shaft. Hole through end of each handle for short loop. Collection of Musical Instruments of Dorothy and Robert Rosenbaum, Scarsdale, 332.

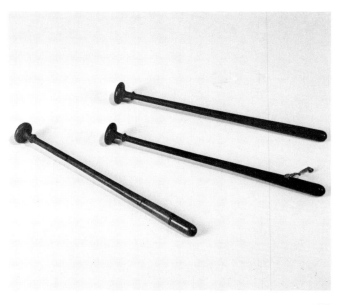

The Classical 1750/1825

It has been said that music is architecture in sound. The term "classical" therefore seems exactly the right way to sum up in a single word the awesome perfection of symmetry and proportion, the balance of unity and contrast, and the relationship of key and contour, that so thoroughly pervades the music of the classical trinity: Haydn, Mozart, and Beethoven. The concept of "classic" seems formal, pretentious, and even aristocratic for some modern realists and pragmatists. That is a pity as well as a naive misconception, for the music does not wear a powdered wig.

With two familiar exceptions, instrumental resources in the Classical period were inherited from the Baroque. By 1709 Bartolommeo Cristofori had invented the piano and had devised such a simple yet ingenious mechanism that his design would remain unchanged in any important way for a hundred years. Although the early "fortepiano" was born in the Baroque, it grew up in the Classical Period and enjoyed a rich and storied fulfillment in the Romantic era. The piano remains a significant medium in the 20th century. The clarinet forms a similar bridge between musical periods. The clarinet was invented about 1700 by Johann Christoph Denner, was thereafter tested and refined and then suddenly elevated to greatness in the Classical Period by Mozart, who also gave the piano its first Olympian music. The clarinet is the only wind instrument since 1800 that has so often attracted major composers: for example, Weber, Brahms, Debussy, Stravinsky, and Berg. The basset horn is a tenor clarinet with a particularly beautiful sound. Although its life was short, Mozart and, in our own century, Richard Strauss gave it lasting importance in the history of musical instruments.

The most important advance in instrument design in the late 18th century had to do not with an instrument as such but with what many of us mistakenly regard as an accessory. Close to a thousand years after the first bow was applied to string instruments, a Frenchman, François Tourte (1747-1835), brought the bow to such perfection of form that it seems unlikely his design will ever be surpassed. String players bestow the ultimate accolade on this great craftsman by calling him "the Stradivari of bow makers".

Toward 1800 began a major upheaval in the design of nearly all musical instruments which was quite unlike anything that had ever taken place before. Political and social changes long in the wind were altering the nature of musical audiences and shifting the performance setting from the salons and palaces of the noble and well-to-do to ever more commodious public galleries. Enlarged bodies of strings may have been dictated by the size of the concert halls or else by the composers' demands for strings to balance the increasingly larger wind sections, but the cause is not as important as the change itself. In the space of a few decades, orchestras doubled and even tripled in size. Composers sought brilliance of orchestral timbre rather than the more mellow, lustrous hues of the

18th century. The most extreme change took place with strings and since the old Italian instruments were much too good to be discarded, within a very short time virtually all violins, even the legendary instruments made in Cremona by the Amati, Guarneri, and Stradivari families, were altered to produce the new sound. The original necks were replaced with new, longer ones set at a greater angle, the bridges were heightened, the fingerboards were lengthened to facilitate a higher range, gut strings were replaced with wire, and both string length and string tension were increased. All of these drastic alterations resulted from a quest for greater volume, a bigger sound, and increased brilliance. Only in very recent years have we begun to convert a few of these instruments back to their original state and to make new instruments in the older model - this in order to restore the warmth and velvety sheen that was an intrinsic ideal in the performance of 18th century music.

Woodwinds, too, reflected the change of taste at the beginning of the nineteenth century. Larger woodwind finger holes produced a bigger sound; woods of greater density had more brilliance; increasingly complex key systems improved intonation, range, and agility. Beethoven himself, usually regarded as the transitional figure from Classical to Romantic music, added the piccolo at one end of the orchestral spectrum and the contrabassoon and three trombones at the other. Trumpets stayed at two or three in number, while horns increased permanently (or at least until Wagner) to four. Opera house orchestras, as usual, pointed the way for their symphonic counterparts by making use of the tenor oboe (misnamed "English horn"), the bass clarinet, and a variety of exotic percussion. The huge 19th century symphony orchestra was almost complete.

Even that relative newcomer, the piano, began to lose its 18th century, compact and transparent tone in favour of the massive sonority required already by Beethoven, then increasingly by the Romantic pianist-composers Schumann, Brahms, Chopin, and Liszt. The piano's range was extended an octave in either direction, and its string tension and thus its power and quality of sound were increased markedly by the addition of a heavy cast iron frame. Small wonder that in the nineteenth century the soft-spoken harpsichord, viol, recorder, and lute seemed quite extinct. How fast things had changed; the first eight Beethoven keyboard sonatas had been written for "pianoforte or harpsichord".

163. FLUTE IN C

August Grenser, Dresden (1720-1807)

The importance of August Grenser and his nephew-successor Heinrich was set forth under No.101. Their flutes Nos.163 and 164 are virtually identical, although made in all likelihood some 20 to 40 years apart. Their respective lengths, including the longest of seven upper joints which accompany each, are only 05 cm. or 1/50 of an inch. These two flutes, one from a major European museum and the other from a major American museum, are in constant use for concerts and recordings by a number of distinguished performers. It appears that more "original instrument" recordings have been made with August Grenser flutes than with those of any other maker, earlier or later.

Alternate upper joints for flutes in particular, but occasionally for oboes and even bassoons, were provided well into the 20th century in order to permit adaptation to the broad range of pitches which were in use before pitch became somewhat standardized. Some flutes had as few as three upper joints of slightly increasing length, while others had as many as seven. These joints made it possible to alter pitch without extending a tenon and socket joint so far as to create a disruptive gap on the inner surface of the bore.

L 63.85 cm. with longest of seven upper joints. Four sections. In fitted case. Boxwood, with ivory mounts. One silver key. Upper joints' lengths: #1 18.5 cm. #2 17.7 cm. #3 17.0 cm. #4 16.2 cm. #5 15.5 cm. #6 14.8 cm. #7 14.0 cm. Rück Collection, Germanisches National-museum, Nürnberg, MIR 297.

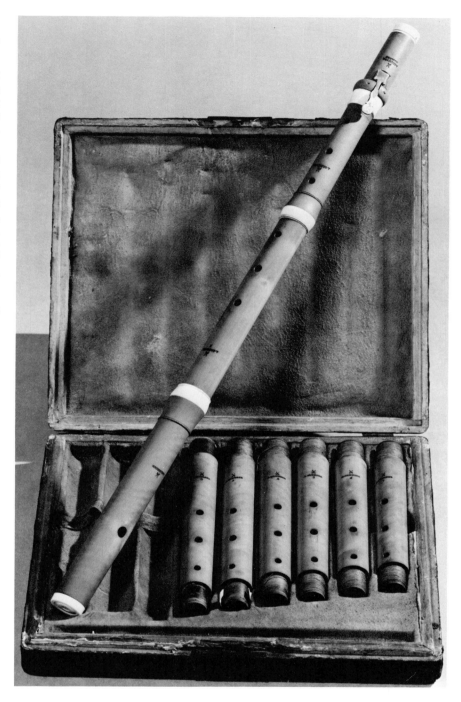

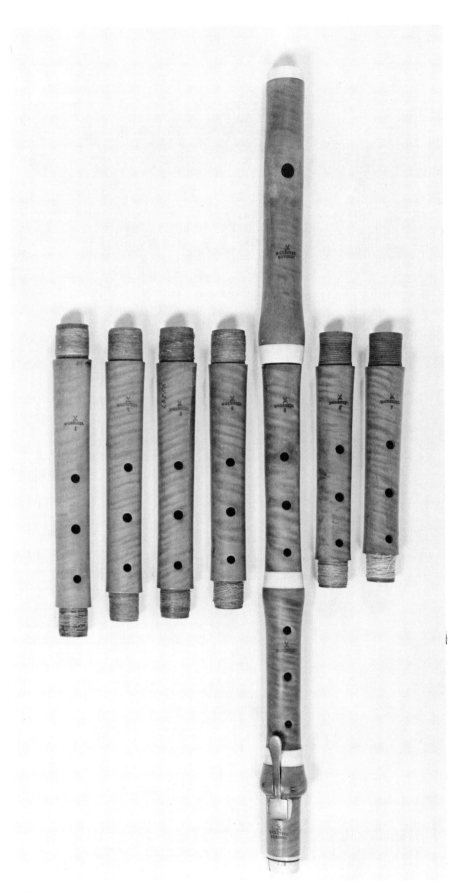

164. FLUTE IN C

Heinrich Grenser, Dresden (1764-1813)

circa 1800

I have not seen a more beautifully grained flute than this. It is not flame-grained or tiger maple but boxwood, which (according to 18th century writers) develops such grain patterns under certain conditions and/or in certain species, the Turkish variety for one. Apart from this remarkable feature, it is all but identical to the preceding example by Heinrich's uncle and teacher.

Both these flutes have a "register" in their foot joints, meaning an extendable inner sleeve with calibrations along its length which serves as an aid to fine tuning. However, the alternate upper joints and "registers" were made obsolete by the "barrel" tuning section built into the lower end of the head joint, which consisted of thin, overlapping metal sleeves that created no significant disruptive gap when extended. This tuning method is still in use today.

Although Heinrich Grenser never stamped a date on his instruments (with one important exception, No. 245), in 1807 he replaced his usual trademark, the crossed swords of Saxony (also used on Dresden china and on nearly all his uncle's instruments) with a Saxon crown, symbolic of his appointment to a court position. Instruments stamped with the crown therefore date from the period 1807-1813, while earlier pieces bear the crossed swords.

Boxwood, with ivory mounts. One silver key. L 63.9 cm. with longest of seven upper joints. Four sections. In roll-up pouch type of case. Division of Musical Instruments, Smithsonian Institution, Washington, D.C., 95.297.

165. FLUTE IN C

Heinrich Grenser, Dresden (1764-1813)

The most interesting thing about this flute has not been previously reported, as far as I know. On all three upper joints it has a hole for the left thumb. (See close-up.) Uncovering this would produce the pitch c'', which otherwise is not well in tune. Philip Bate's definitive book on the flute is the best source of explanation but does not specifically deal with this "improvement" in fingering. (See pp. 98 and 226 of the first edition.) This extra hole could be given to the left thumb since b♭' is here given to the right forefinger.

Otherwise this is the popular six-keyed flute, ca. 1800. Heinrich made other flutes with as many as eight keys and, as we have seen with No. 164, as few as the one key for d#'. On this present specimen, the foot joint has been extended and a key provided for low c. All six of the keys are original, and are mounted in integral blocks. There are actually only five flaps, but the f' flap is controlled by either of two touches.

Boxwood, with ivory mounts. Six silver keys. No register. L 65.1 cm. with the longest of three upper joints. Four sections. Musikmuseet, Stockholm, 22649.

166. FLUTE IN C

Friedrich Gabriel August Kirst (1750-1806)

Kirst is a most interesting maker, known particularly for his handsome flutes but deserving greater appreciation for other woodwinds as well. His teacher was August Grenser, obviously some years before Heinrich Grenser was old enough to begin such an apprenticeship, and it is fascinating to observe August's characteristics which occur more frequently on later instruments by one disciple or the other. The several specimens in *The Look of Music* afford a special opportunity for such comparison. Also of interest is a strong, perhaps only coincidental similarity between the few surviving flutes made by Quantz and a number of those by Kirst. Both men lived in Potsdam, possibly even (briefly) at the same time.

Ebony, with ivory mounts. One silver key. Four sections. No register. L 63.64 cm. with longest of four upper joints 16.4 cm. 15.7 cm. 15.0 cm. and 14.26 cm. Musikinstrumenten Museum des Staatlichen Institut f. Musikforschung — Preussischer Kulturbesitz, Berlin, 4895.

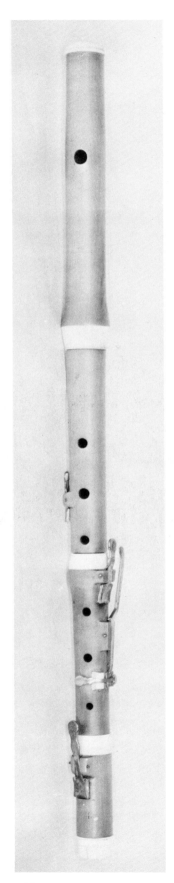
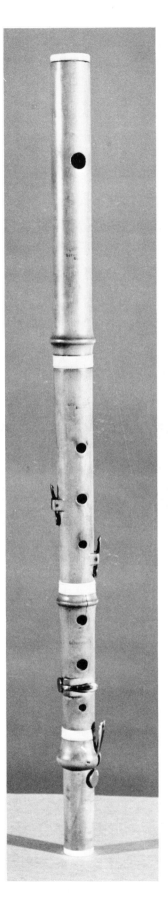

167. FLUTE IN C

Friedrich Gabriel August Kirst, Potsdam (1750-1806)

This is not one of Kirst's prettier flutes but was chosen because it has not been illustrated previously or seen in the West. One may be quite sure that it originally had additional upper joints, since lost. It has a register in the foot joint. The flute began life with only four keys, but a fifth (touch) was added to activate the f' flap by the left little finger. This added lever is mounted in an ivory saddle (vs. the integral block used on the preceding flute for the same duplicate touch.)

Boxwood, with ivory mounts. Four silver keys originally, to which a fifth touch has been added. Four sections. Register. L 60.7 cm. Institute of Theatre, Music, and Cinematography, Leningrad, 1136.

168. FLUTE IN C

Asa Hopkins, Litchfield, Connecticut (1779-1839)

American woodwind makers followed English models with few exceptions, and during roughly the first half of the 19th century were reasonably successful. Lowered tariffs on imports from abroad then wiped them off the scene until the 20th century. Hopkins was a mechanical genius, in the opinion of many contemporaries, and first distinguished himself in the highly competitive field of clock-making, then turned to woodwinds. It seems possible that he was the first to introduce the principle of interchangeable parts for woodwinds, as his friend Eli Whitney had done in the mass manufacture of rifles and as Hopkins himself had taken steps to do in clock-making. His principal workshop stood until very recently and was about the size of a two-car garage. As his employees gradually built their homes around this factory the village thus created became known as "Fluteville" and is still so identified on maps of the area.

Boxwood, with ivory mounts. Four brass keys. Four sections. L 61.0 cm. Collection of Musical Instruments of Dorothy and Robert Rosenbaum, Scarsdale, 24a.

169. OBOE

William Milhouse, Newark (...1763-1800...)

Oboes with a fairly straight, unadorned form like this (as opposed to the decorative "bulb" or "onion" or "cotton spool" types with prominent turnings) are known as the English straight model. They appear to have been made only (or mainly?) during the middle to late 18th century, by major makers such as Stanesby Jr., Collier, and Milhouse. Straight models by one or another Milhouse seem to pre-date 1800, but there may indeed be exceptions. The design has never seemed as pleasing visually as the infinite variations otherwise seen on 18th and early 19th century oboes.

William Milhouse seems to be the earliest woodwind maker of this name, but there is a Richard, who apparently (like William) worked first in Newark and then London, and an H. Milhouse and Sons of London slightly later. William's dates are so broad as to suggest a son or grandson or other successor who continued under that name. Makers of that surname have been unusually prolific.

Pearwood?, with ivory mounts. Three sections. Two brass keys. H 58.1 cm. Bate Collection, Oxford, 26.

170. OBOE

William Milhouse, London (...1763-1800...)

This specimen serves nicely to support my preference for oboes with decorative turnings. The overall effect here is not of extravagance but, on the contrary, of pleasing proportion between simple line and graceful swells. The lovely wood tone is a perfect setting for the elegant yet simple silver key shapes. Silver keys, especially on English instruments, were often made by silversmiths on order from the instrument maker and sometimes carry the traditional hallmark of their maker. On oboes in particular, silver keys and/or ivory mounts were extras for which an additional charge was made, and were therefore used mainly by well-to-do amateurs. The unmounted boxwood instrument with brass keys was the journeyman instrument and today usually shows signs of heavier use.

Boxwood, unmounted. Two silver keys. Three sections. H 56.9 cm. School of Music, University of Victoria, 1976-14.

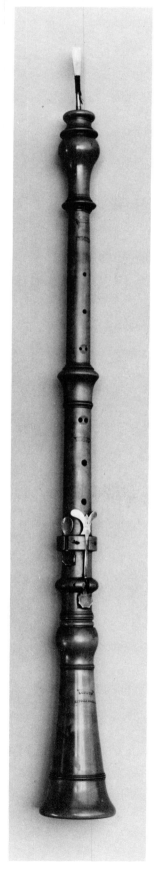

171. OBOE

Lutringer

This maker's name is listed in Langwill's *Index* but his dates, place of work, and nationality are all unknown. Furthermore, this is the only known instrument by him. The oboe was part of the old Kraus Collection in Florence, and it must be from that catalogue that Mr. Langwill learned of its existence. It has not been exhibited in modern times, as far as can be determined. Langwill reports that the name may be "L. UTRINGER" or "LUTRINGER". After much study and repeated examination, I believe it is the latter and shall so list it here.

To date it approximately or fix its country of origin is another matter. Its two keys suggest mid-18th century, but the bell shape and turnings seem earlier. They remind one very much of Stanesby Sr. (No. 90), in fact. The Kraus label says "English?" There is a certain resemblance to "Type A" early English oboes as illustrated in the Galpin Society *Journal,* Volume II. On the other hand, the maker's stamp has raised letters with the area surrounding depressed by the stamp, and this style is more often used by Italian makers (Rafi and Anciuti, for example).

Further detective work is needed, obviously. These comments have been offered here to show how much there is still to be learned.

Boxwood? with tortoise shell finish, unmounted. Two brass keys, but the eb touch is broken off and not preserved. Three sections. H 54.5 cm. Private collection, Vancouver.

172. OBOE

Jakob Grundmann, Dresden (1729-1800)

Dated 1797

This maker enjoyed an enviable reputation in his own day and for some time thereafter as a specialist in oboes. He is credited with being among the first, perhaps even the first, to add various new keys to the two-keyed oboe and seems likely to have developed an improved bore design as well. One of the surest testimonials to his achievements is the frequency with which additional keys have been added in several stages, evidence that the instrument played especially well and its owners were anxious to keep on using it.

The overall body profile and the ten keys on this instrument are quite lovely, although it is almost certain that some of the keys are later additions. In contrast to many such improvements, however, these additions are done in immaculate taste. They match the original keys in the colour of the brass, the shape of both flaps and touches, and the quality of finish. It seems very likely that the additional keys, if not original, were added by Grundmann's successors, who were trained by him; first J.F. Floth (No. 177) and then, in 1807, C.G. Bormann. The long key for c#' is precisely where later would have been located the long b♮ key, the absence of which here suggests early rather than much later modification of Grundmann's original key layout.

Boxwood, with ivory mounts. Three sections. Ten brass keys mounted in knobs, blocks, and brass saddles. Brass thumb rest, as well. H 56.8 cm. Museum für Hamburgische Geschichte, Hamburg, 1912.1551.

173. OBOE

Jakob Grundmann, Dresden (1729-1800)

Dated 17??

This is certainly an early Grundmann oboe, judging by its various body contours. The bell is somewhat concave, which is characteristic of Grundmann in the '60s and early '70s, after which he seems to have developed the convex profile that was soon adopted by his competitors as well. The bell is original, and carries the usual Grundmann stamp and the date, as was the maker's laudable practice. I believe that further study will enable us to determine accurately which additional keys were added to oboes at various precise dates, thanks to the combination of Grundmann's dated instruments and his established place at the forefront of oboe improvement. It may also be possible to read the (thus far) illegible two final digits of the date on this instrument, perhaps under ultraviolet light.

One cannot fail to notice on this instrument a hodge-podge of different key shapes and styles, in contrast to the preceding instrument. This was originally a two-keyed oboe, those keys being the lower two, ignoring the very long key on the right. The others are considerably later additions, many of them mounted on posts and axles. These in particular indicate a long playing life for this oboe.

Boxwood, unmounted. Three sections. Nine brass keys, of which seven are judged to be later additions. H 56.8 cm. Institute of Theatre, Music, and Cinematography, Leningrad, 518.

174. OBOE

Jakob Grundmann, Dresden (1729-1800)

Dated 1799

This instrument again illustrates the point that an oboe particularly valued for its playing qualities might well have keys added at several later stages. Originally this one had two keys, like No. 173. The two uppermost keys and perhaps the one that is mounted in the widely flared centre knob were next, followed by the others either separately or in a single modernization. Note the amputation performed on one of the swallowtail key's tails.

Grundmann did indeed concentrate on various types of oboe, but is survived as well by a few each of basset horns (No. 186), clarinets, bassoons, and a single flute. As was pointed out under No. 82, Grundmann, along with August Grenser, was a student of Johann Poerschman in Leipzig. The wonder is that two apprentices would leave the nest for the same destination, where they must surely have been competitors for 50 years.

Boxwood, unmounted. Three sections. Eleven silver keys, but originally just two. H 56.5 cm. Museum für Hamburgische Geschichte, Hamburg, 1912.1552.

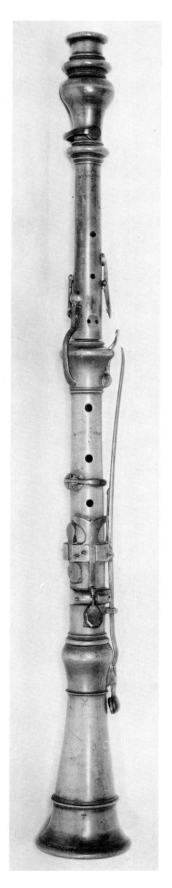

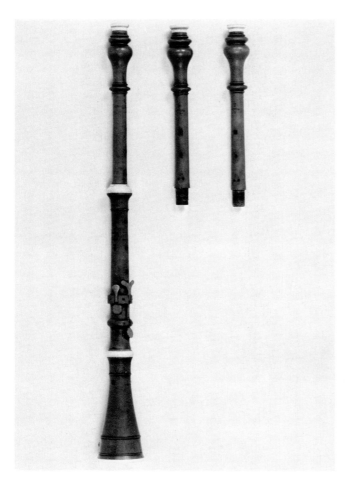

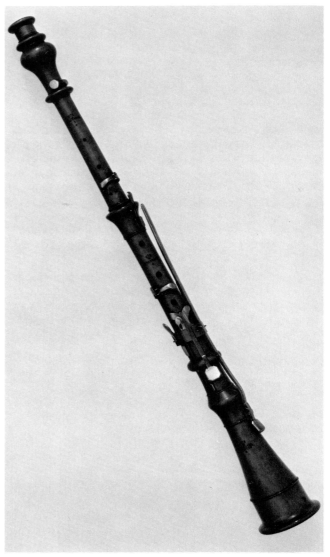

175. OBOE

Christophe Delusse, Paris (. . .1758-1790. . .)

The importance of this Parisian maker is just beginning to be understood, I think. Not only do his instruments play exceptionally well today, but they also reflect a very high level of craftsmanship and show their maker's propensity for the kind of experimentation that produced significant advances in oboe design. As was pointed out in the remarks that introduce the Classical Period, Delusse's tools were eventually bought by young Henri Brod, thus directly linking the mid-18th century to the modern Lorée. Michel Piguet has chosen a Delusse oboe from his collection for several of the exceptional recordings he has made recently, notably the Mozart Oboe Quartet. The present oboe was both owned and used by Auguste-Gustave Vogt (1781-1870), one of the great oboists of all time. This oboe retains three alternate upper joints, not nearly as common a way for oboes to adjust pitch as for flutes. Several keys added to the instrument at a later time have now been removed.

Boxwood, with ivory mounts. Three sections. Two brass keys. A later f#' and b♮ have been removed. H 56.5 cm. with longest upper joint. Musée Instrumental du Conservatoire de Paris, E.387, C.480.

176. OBOE

Heinrich Grenser, Dresden (1764-1813)

After 1806

This oboe proves that Heinrich Grenser learned not only from his uncle August, but (unofficially) from Grundmann as well. Many external features, at least, are adopted from the rival(?) maker and are not found on the uncle's oboes; the widely flared, narrow centre knob, for example. It is possible that all eight keys are original, but the presence of a now-plugged tuning hole in the bell in addition to that used for low b♮ suggests that this key at least is an addition. On the other hand, the octave key hole has what appears to be an integral, raised seat and so is certainly original. This oboe has a crown above the maker's name in the stamp and so, as explained under No. 164, was made between 1807 and 1813.

Boxwood, unmounted. Three sections. Eight brass keys, perhaps only four originally. H 55.8 cm. Metropolitan Museum of Art, New York, X307.

177. OBOE

Johann Friedrich Floth, Dresden (1761-1807)

Floth apprenticed under Grundmann and was his partner for 17 years until Grundmann's death, according to Langwill. Even so, only "GRUNDMANN" appears on any instrument made prior to the older partner's death, at which point "FLOTH ET GRUNDMANN" (and the reverse) was used briefly, soon followed by "FLOTH" alone. The partners' instruments are all but indistinguishable from each other and from those by Floth's successor, Carl Gottlob Bormann. At least six of the nine keys here are original, the ones likely to have been added being low b♮, c#', and f#', all of which are in the style of the original keys and beautifully made.

Boxwood, unmounted. Three sections. Nine silver keys. H. 56.5 cm. Yale University, Collection of Musical Instruments, New Haven, 196.

178. CLARINET IN B

Mousetter, Paris (. . .1770?. . .)

Mousetter's clarinet was first illustrated in Anthony Baines' *Woodwind Instruments and Their History*. However, little is known of Mousetter. This is a typical continental five-keyed clarinet with a longer barrel joint and rounder (almost oval) main knob that can be seen in the typical English design of the following two instruments. Mousetter is also survived by a flute in Berlin.

Boxwood, unmounted. Five brass keys. Six sections. H 61.2 cm. excluding mouthpiece. Bate Collection, Oxford, 406.

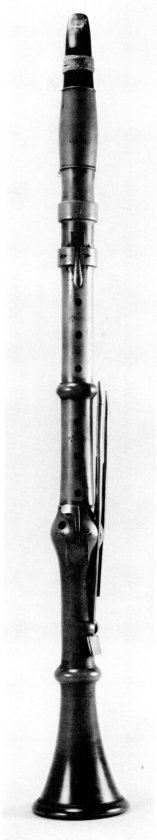

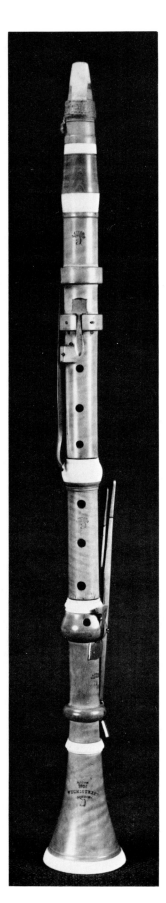

179. CLARINET IN C

Asa Hopkins, Litchfield, Connecticut (1779-1839)

A consideration of this maker was included under No. 168. One should not overlook the steady development, as opposed to feverish proliferation, of clarinet keys during the 18th century. Although clarinets are not grouped together in *The Look of Music* but are shown with their contemporary woodwind voices, there is a clear evolution from Denner's two-keyed chalumeau (No. 52), to Kenigsperger's three-keyed clarinet (No. 100), to August Grenser's four-keyed instrument (No. 101), to this five-keyed clarinet, and then to the six-keyed model on the following page. After that, additional keys came much more rapidly and were designed mainly for trills. The clarinet in C was extremely popular, perhaps especially for use in military and village bands. Occasionally one finds cased sets of three: C, Bb, and A, versus the standard Bb and A set that is required by players today.

Boxwood, with ivory mounts. Rosewood mouthpiece. Five brass keys. H 59.2 cm. including mouthpiece. School of Music, University of Victoria, 1970-6.

180. CLARINET IN C & Bb

George Astor, London (ca 1760-ca 1830)

Astor immigrated from Germany to England and founded a woodwind making business, later to expand to pianos and organs as well. Soon after arriving in London, George sent for his younger brother to help in the new business, but this proved to be only a temporary aid. The younger brother shortly headed off to America, carrying a few of his brother's woodwinds wrapped in a blanket to sell upon arrival. On the boat to the New World, however, another immigrant advised him to forget musical instruments and go into the fur trade "where the money was". The advice was taken, and produced one of the earliest legendary American multimillionaires, John Jacob Astor. Woodwinds were not completely forgotten, however, Astor himself tells of sitting around Indian campfires while on fur-trading expeditions, and playing his flute to the delight of his hosts.

This handsome instrument is provided with alternate upper joints of considerable difference in length and also alternate middle joints, with the result that it can be switched to either a C or Bb instrument. An extra compartment in the case suggests that a further joint is missing and might have permitted switching to A-pitch as well. As on the Mousetter clarinet (No. 178), the two long keys for the left little finger have extendable shanks to allow for the difference in reach when using alternate sections of various lengths.

Boxwood, with ivory mounts. Six sections when the instrument is fully assembled. Six brass keys. H: in C 54.0 cm. and in Bb 59.5 cm., both measurements not including mouthpiece. Bate Collection, Oxford, 4.

181. CLARINET IN Bb & A

Heinrich Grenser, Dresden (1764-1813)

As with the Astor clarinet preceding, this lovely instrument can be assembled to play in either of two keys, here Bb or A. Then as now, the serious clarinetist needed both if he was to play the standard orchestral or solo repertoire. The A clarinet has a richer, darker sound than the Bb and so is dictated by composers in works where they deem those characteristics desirable, while the Bb clarinet has a slightly more brilliant tone, sometimes equally appropriate. Furthermore, if the composer has no particular predilection toward one or the other, he can vastly simplify the clarinetist's assignment by writing for whichever pitch puts the clarinet into the easier key to finger. This is no small favour!

This is a late Heinrich Grenser instrument and shows well the beauty, clean design, and functional simplicity of his instruments, even though ever more keys were required as the instrument makers sought improved intonation, reliability and flexibility.

Boxwood, with ivory mounts. Six sections when fully assembled. The mouthpiece is a replacement. Eleven brass keys. H (in A) 67.0 cm. with mouthpiece. Wilhelm Heckel KG, Biebrich, K-7.

182. CLARINET IN Bb

Heinrich Grenser, Dresden (1764-1813)

1807-1813

This instrument is very similar to the preceding specimen, but is only in Bb without the A alternative. Eventually it was found that one clarinet could *not* do the work of two. Proportions between various tone holes, the mouthpiece, and bore were simply too critical to permit compromises. Today, the serious clarinetist carries two complete instruments for Bb and A respectively to every job. Players use a common mouthpiece only because of the finicky and recalcitrant reed. Two keys are missing here of the original nine, and the mouthpiece is a replacement.

Boxwood, with ivory mounts. Nine brass keys. H 59.3 cm. without mouthpiece. Bate Collection, Oxford, 432.

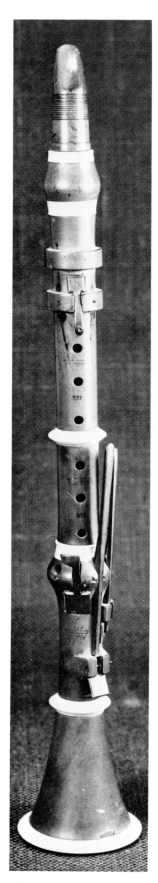
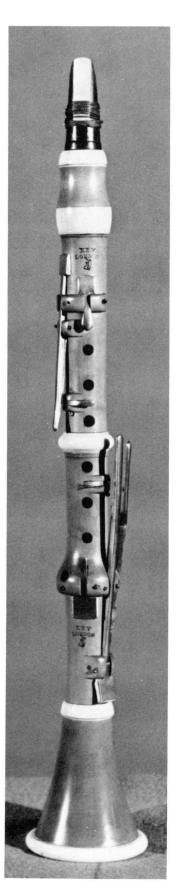

183. CLARINET IN Eb

Griessling & Schlott (1771-1835) and (-1843), Berlin

Unlike high-pitched small bassoons (Nos. 49 and 104) for which there is no specific role, smaller clarinets in D, E, F, and even higher pitches, were actually called for in certain compositions, as they are today occasionally. The higher the pitch of clarinet, of course, the more shrill and difficult to play in tune. The respected firm of Griessling and Schlott were important makers of both woodwinds and brasses.

Boxwood, with ivory mounts. Five brass keys. Six sections when fully assembled. H 44.0 cm. without mouthpiece. Bate Collection, Oxford, 4004.

184. CLARINET IN F

Thomas Key, London (. . .1800-1850. . .)

Another small, high clarinet is this lovely specimen in F. This one is comprised of just five sections instead of six, and its keys are mounted in integral blocks and knobs, unusual for so late an instrument. Key is also represented in *The Look of Music* by a bassoon, No. 192, and a valve horn, No. 263.

Boxwood, with ivory mounts. Eight brass keys. H 44.2 cm. including mouthpiece. Collection of Musical Instruments of Dorothy and Robert Rosenbaum, Scarsdale, 118.

185. BASSET HORN

Anton Sr. et Michael Mayrhofer, Passau (1706-1774) and (1707-1778)

Four curved, leather-covered clarinet-type instruments exist with the stamp "ANTON et MICHAEL MAYR-HOFER, INVENTORS AND MAKERS, PASSAU". Two of these are included in *The Look of Music* and, in view of their rarity, represent one of the more remarkable features of this exhibition. One, almost certainly the earliest of the four, is No. 244 and will be described in a different context. This one is that wonderful child of the Classical Period, a basset horn, in all likelihood the very first, or failing that, the second. In any event, the tenor clarinet or "basset horn" - a fifth, or occasionally a fourth, lower than the standard soprano, but retaining the soprano's dispropor-tionately narrow bore and the warmth of its lower register - became a unique, if limited, classical voice. *The Look of Music* includes four, all made within a 50-year period. The basset horn is an anachronism that has never lost its haun-ting, sensuous tone, and for which a small number of indescribably beautiful pieces exist which can be perform-ed so well on no modern instrument. The great composer for basset horn was Mozart.

Maple, with brass mounts. Six brass keys. L air column (estimated) 113.0 cm. Bore 1.25-1.3 cm. Germanisches Nationalmuseum, Nürnberg, MI 133.

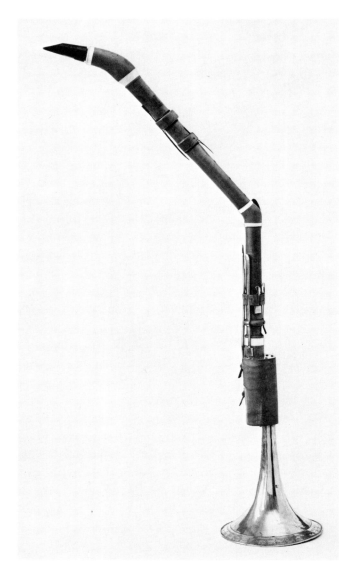

186. BASSET HORN

Jakob Grundmann, Dresden (1729-1800)

Dated 1787

The first basset horns (see the preceding instrument) were curved, sickle-shape, wrapped with leather, cornett style (Nos. 13-16). To avoid too cumbersome length, the lower portion was doubled back on itself within a triple-bored (rackett-like, as in No. 103) *kasten,* thereby compressing the lower tube into one-third of its actual length. Curved tubes were difficult to make and prone to leaking, so the next and virtually final step was the angular form, of which this and the next two examples are typical. On the *kasten* are mounted supplementary basset keys that extend the range several notes lower, and below the *kasten* is a brass, flared bell.

After this model, a few were made that resembled narrower, shorter, modern bass clarinets. They survived into this century principally in the opera orchestra of Richard Strauss. There they defy substitution by any other instru-

ment. How strange that such a singularly evocative and effective voice has no other modern identity!

Boxwood, with ivory mounts. Seven sections. Eight brass keys. Length over outside of knee, bell rim to mouthpiece tip, 103.0 cm. Bore 1.5 cm. Museum für Hamburgische Geschichte, Hamburg, 1912.1560.

187. BASSET HORN

Heinrich Grenser, Dresden (1764-1813)

by 1807

This basset horn has an oval bell, designed to take up less space between the player's legs when held in that position. This has always seemed to me to resemble an oval baseball, an oval wheel, or an oval timpani. Even so, it works.

Even more practical and utilitarian is a homemade thumb rest on the back of the tube of this instrument, made out of a bottle cap labelled "Rheims 1864".

Boxwood, with horn mounts and ivory knee and mouthpiece. Eight brass keys. Seven sections. L (air column) 105.95 cm. Bore 1.42 cm. Bate Collection, Oxford, 489.

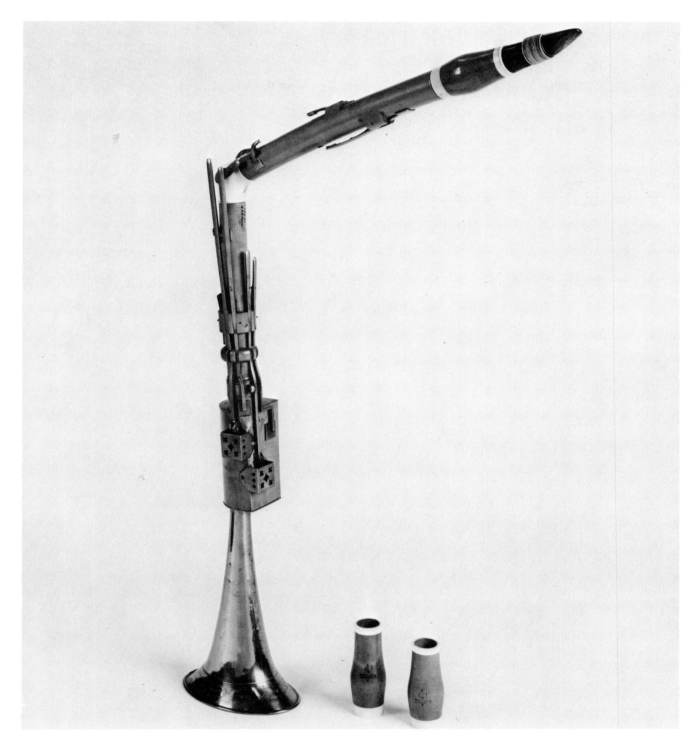

188. BASSET HORN

Griessling & Schlott (1771-1835) and (-1843), Berlin

This instrument is slightly later than the preceding two, has four additional keys and is nearly a right-angle in form, but otherwise is unchanged. The alternate barrels are for changing overall pitch. This is a cumbersome-looking instrument although beautifully made and preserved, and it is hard to imagine a player holding it with any feeling of stability or balance. This must be what prompted a few makers in the early 19th century to redesign the basset horn in bassoon shape and then to turn to the long straight body with curved neck and bell, in which form the instrument is made in small numbers today.

Boxwood, with ivory mounts. Seven sections. Twelve brass keys. L with shortest barrel 108.0 cm. Bore 1.52 cm. Division of Musical Instruments, Smithsonian Institution, Washington, D.C., 384.091

155

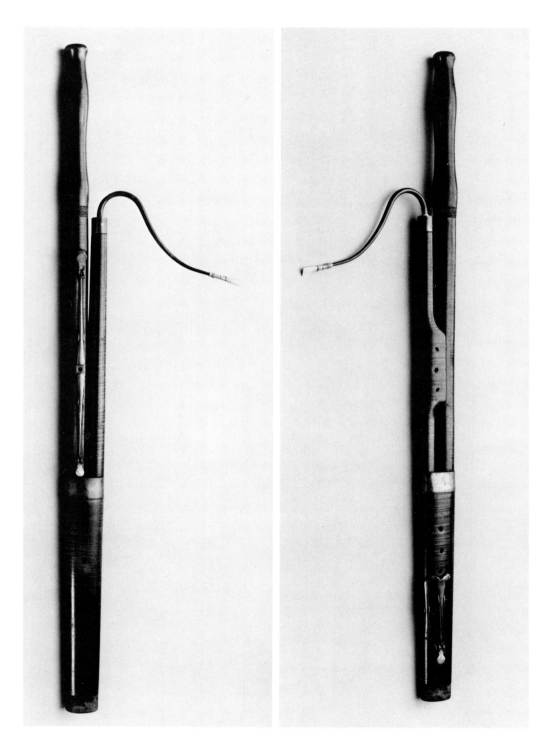

189. BASSOON

John Blockley, Ullesthorpe, Leicester (1735-1798)

This can be identified as one of the earlier English bassoons, not only because it has just four keys but also because of its bell shape and the separation between the tops of the wing and bass joints. These characteristics were supplanted by another model (of which No. 192 is typical)

that became the standard English bassoon well into the 19th century, regardless of the number of keys that were added. John Blockley is known by just four instruments: besides this one, a flute, an oboe, and a tenor bassoon. This instrument was formerly in the collection of Anthony Baines and was a gift to the present owner.

Maple, with brass mounts. Four brass keys. H 122.8 cm. Prof. and Mrs. Phillip T. Young, Victoria.

190. BASSOON

August Grenser, Dresden (1720-1807)

Dated 1779

Of some 15 bassoons by August Grenser that are known, I think this one is the most beautiful. The elegant ivory keys are unusual enough, but there is a tasteful degree of ornamentation that is characteristic of this maker in particular. (Of his two principal apprentices, Kirst followed in that direction more than nephew Heinrich.) Examples of Grenser's style are the notches along the shanks of the keys and the carving on the flat table of the bass joint. It is remarkable how few bassoons of any vintage have any surface decoration whatever.

The two brass keys on the wing joint are obvious later additions. Unlike Grundmann, August Grenser did not routinely date his instruments, but fortunately a number of his bassoons do have a date.

Maple, with brass mounts, Five ivory keys and two brass keys added later on the wing joint. H 124.5 cm. Musée Instrumental du Conservatoire de Paris, E.188, C.505.

191. BASSOON

Heinrich Grenser, Dresden (1764-1813)

Before 1807

The celebrated "Dresdener fagott" was the product of August and perhaps especially Heinrich Grenser, even though its reputation must not cause us to forget the remarkable quality of their other instruments. It is not mere coincidence that Karl Almenraeder, "the father of the German bassoon", began his experiments *with* and *on* a bassoon by Heinrich; obviously it was the best instrument available at the time. This present specimen is a particularly handsome one, I think. A ninth key of brass was added for C# L4 and tastefully covered with boxwood to blend in with the original boxwood keys. The bell profile is characteristic of mature Heinrich Grenser bassoons and was widely copied by other makers of the time.

Tiger maple, with brass mounts. Eight boxwood keys, plus one key added later. H 126.1 cm. Haags Gemeentemuseum, Holland, Ea 570-1933.

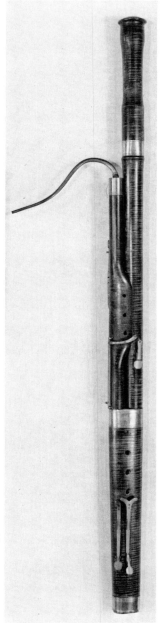

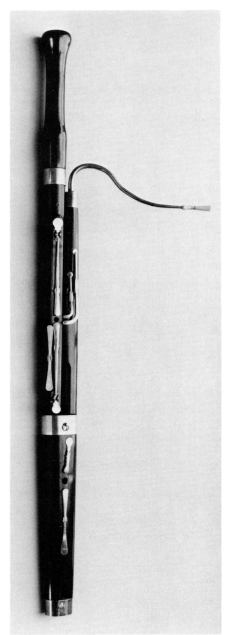

192. BASSOON

Friedrich Gabriel August Kirst, Potsdam (1750-1806)

This bassoon shows very nicely the influence of Kirst's teacher, August Grenser, especially in the shape and decorated edges of its handsome keys. This instrument has been much used, as one can see from the worn fingerholes. Another Kirst bassoon is dated 1801, and proves thereby that he still made bassoons even after he became admired as a flute maker.

Maple, with brass mounts. Six brass keys. H 123.4 cm. Museum für Hamburgische Geschichte, Hamburg, 1928.387.

193. BASSOON

Thomas Key, London (. . .1800-1850. . .)

This is a typical English bassoon of the model that succeeded the earliest sort, No. 189. The bulge below the rim of the bell has disappeared leaving an elongated, slim funnel, and the wing joint fits against the bass joint very snugly all along its length. Other characteristics are compared in the definitive study by the late Eric Halfpenny that appeared in The Galpin Society *Journal*, Volume X. Thomas Key is also represented in *The Look of Music* by the small clarinet in F, No. 184 and a valve horn, No. 263.

H 122.1 cm. School of Music, University of Victoria, 1970-1.

194. CONTRABASSOON

Kaspar Tauber, Vienna (1758-1827)

Earlier contrabassoons are quite rare, the three best known being that by Andreas Eichentopf dated 1714, that by Stanesby Jr. dated 1739 (now in the National Museum, Dublin), and the fanciful, dragon-headed oddity by Anciuti, now in Salzburg. This present example is characteristic of the Viennese contra that Beethoven introduced into the symphony orchestra in his Fifth Symphony. Unlike the earlier three cited above and No. 195, this instrument compresses the required 4.8 metres by using a second butt or boot joint upside-down to bring the (otherwise) upper end of the wing joint back down toward the level of the player's lips.

This contra was found in 1964 in an antique shop on Third Avenue in New York City, to which it had just been brought from Vienna.

Maple, with brass mounts. Eight sections including crook and its extension. Five brass keys, to low D only. H 166.5 cm. Bate Collection, Oxford, 344.

195. CONTRABASSOON IN F (QUINT BASSOON)

Heinrich Grenser II (Heinrich Otto Grenser) (1808- ?)

Since my inventory of Grenser instruments appeared in The Galpin Society *Journal*, Volume XXXI, it has become likely that the stamp on this instrument and on at least three others is that of Heinrich's son, Heinrich Otto. Instead of the traditional crossed swords or the later crown used by the father, this stamp has an eight-pointed star above and below the H. GRENSER name.

This instrument follows the traditional bassoon form rather than the doubled-back upper sections used by Tauber (No. 194), Küss (No. 259) and Stehle (No. 260) and is interesting partly for that reason.

Maple, with brass mounts. Five brass keys. Four sections plus crook. H 186.6 cm. Musée Instrumental, Brussels, 1000.

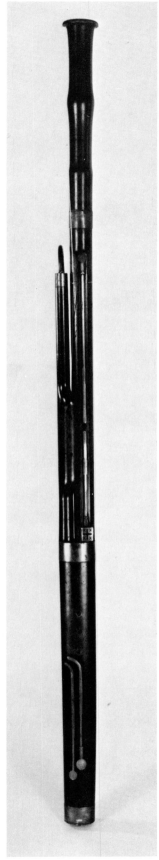

196. HUNTING HORN IN D

Carlin, Paris (?   -1780)

ca 1755-60

A horn of this sort was made to be taken on the hunt and played out to the side, the coils held horizontal by supporting them on the raised arm. The lengthy tube is actually made of seven sections, of which the middle five are cylindrical but of increasing diameter. This is the so-called three-coil horn and very similar to the horn by Daniel Kodisch (No. 110) exhibited as a Baroque instrument. This instrument was formerly in the collection of R. Morley-Pegge and is illustrated in the Fifth Edition of *Grove's Dictionary* as well as in Mr. Morley-Pegge's book *The Horn*.

Actual inscription on bell: *Fait a Paris par Carlin Ordinaire du Roy rue Croix Despetits Champs (fleurs de lis)*

Brass. Coil D. 35.7, bell D. 26.5, tube L. 475 cm. Bate Collection, Oxford, 64.

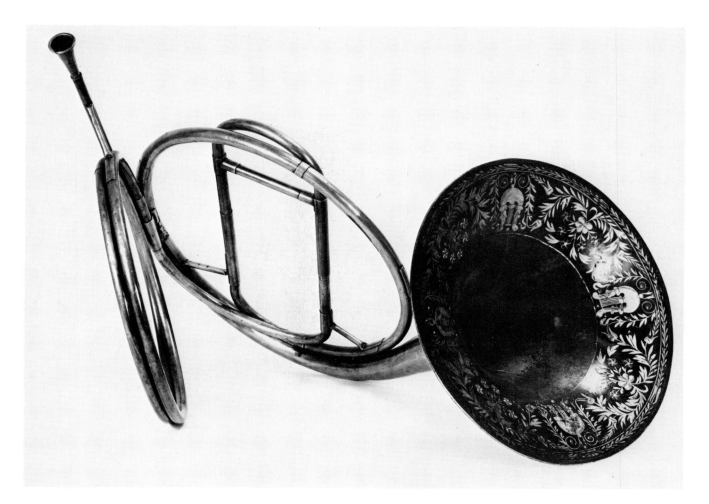

197. ORCHESTRAL HORN

Courtois, Paris

ca. 1820

This instrument is designed to use additional crooks between the mouthpiece and mouthpipe for making changes of key, although it has a tuning slide for fine adjustment built into the centre of the coil. Its mouthpiece is made of sheet brass, not cast brass, and is typical of horn mouthpieces at this time. The enamel decoration of the inner bell surface is also typical and nicely done. The Courtois name is still found on modern brass instruments made in Paris, although no members of the original family are still involved. As with the preceding instrument, this horn was formerly in the collection of R. Morley-Pegge and is illustrated in the same publications.

Actual inscription on bell: *Courtois neveu aine, rue des Vieux Augustins a Paris* (stars).

Brass. Bell with enamelled floral design in red and gold. Dia 30.2 cm. Bell dia 28.5 cm. One coil. Nine crooks. Bate Collection, Oxford, 6.

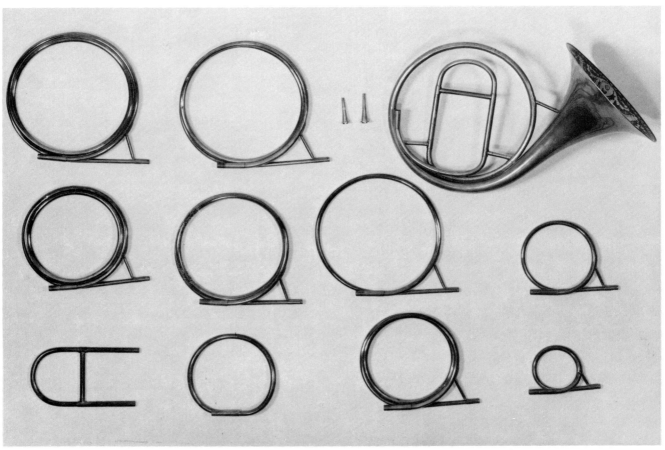

198. ORCHESTRAL HORN

D. Jahn, Paris (. . .1820-1859)

ca 1825

This similar specimen is quite as beautiful as the preceding one and in fact has a remarkably similar bell painting. Although not illustrated in any of the standard books on musical instruments, this horn (then the property of a New York antique dealer) was used as a prop in an illustration featuring transistor radios for an S. & H. Greenstamp Catalogue. The case is presumably original but has been relined.

The Sheldon Collection, Smithsonian Institution, Washington, D.C., 1978.6090

199. ORCHESTRAL HORN

Michael Saurle, Munich (ca 1790-ca 1861)

ca 1815

This horn is without bell decoration but shows well the quality of work typical of this important maker. Long after various designs were out of date for regular use, brass makers were expected to furnish obsolete types for ceremonial use, a phenomenon unknown with woodwinds. Thus Michael Saurle is represented in *The Look of Music* by a large coil hunting horn that might have been used circa 1750 (No. 109), by this orchestral horn with crooks of a type common circa 1790, and yet was an important maker of other instruments that employed various types of valves.

Coil dia. 29.5 cm. Bell dia. 26.8 cm. Rück Collection, Germanisches Nationalmuseum, Nürnberg, MIR 85.

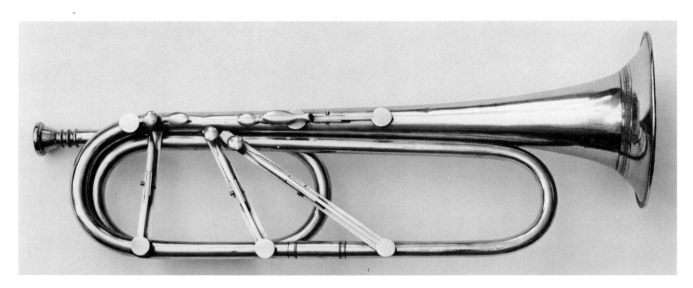

200. KEYED TRUMPET

Anonymous

One rivulet in the search for a means of producing the full chromatic series on brass instruments other than the trombone, was the placing of holes along the tube at appropriate locations and devising keys to control their opening or closing, as on woodwinds. This resulted in the keyed

trumpet and keyed bugle (Nos. 276 and 277). The former is generally acknowledged to be the impetus for Joseph Haydn's beloved *Trumpet Concerto*. Until the keyed instrument appeared, there was no way in which diatonic, much less chromatic, passages could be played except in the extremely high register.

Brass body and six brass keys in saddles. L 42.2 cm. Bell dia 12.2 cm. Musikhistorisk Museum og Carl Claudius' Samling, Copenhagen, F-69.

201. KEYED TRUMPET IN E♭

Anonymous, German or Austrian?

circa 1830

There are surely more important unanswered questions, but why are most keyed trumpets not marked with their maker's name? In my experience, perhaps only five percent or less are marked, yet brass makers (as well as string and keyboard makers) began marking their instruments much earlier than did woodwind makers. No logical ex-

planation occurs to me, unless it is that most keyed trumpets were made for military bands, and the instruments were therefore no great source of pride to their makers. This is not a very convincing explanation.

This particular instrument is made for a left-handed player or a least to be fingered from the left side. On a four-keyed model, rather than five or six, there is a harpsichord-like "short octave" at the lower end.

L 45.1 cm. Rück Collection, Germanisches Nationalmuseum, Nürnberg, MIR 129.

 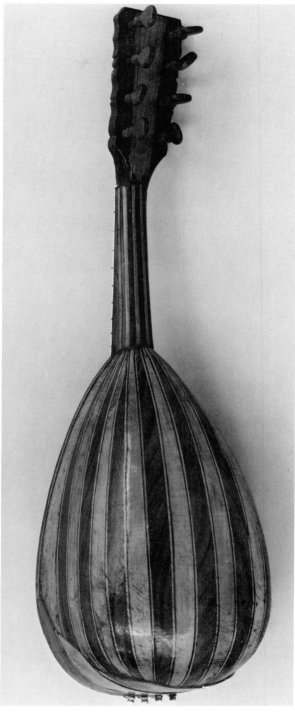

202. MANDOLIN

Anonymous, Italian

Late 18th century

Few would claim that the mandolin is capable of the subtlety and expressiveness of the guitar, but it too has experienced alternating periods of popularity and neglect during its 250-year European history. It is believed to have existed in the Near East before that. Although there are many variations in its stringing and construction, the man-dolin usually employs a plectrum and four courses of double strings, each pair tuned in unison, thereby permitting an effect of sustained sound by rapid movement from one string to the other of the pair. It is essentially a melody instrument, although lower-pitched models exist that are designed to accompany the higher in mandolin bands. Wire strings and frets and a deeply vaulted body (compared with a lute, for example) are characteristic of all mandolins.

Overall L 58.1 cm. Belly W 17.1 cm. Body H ca. 12.0 cm. Private collection, Vancouver.

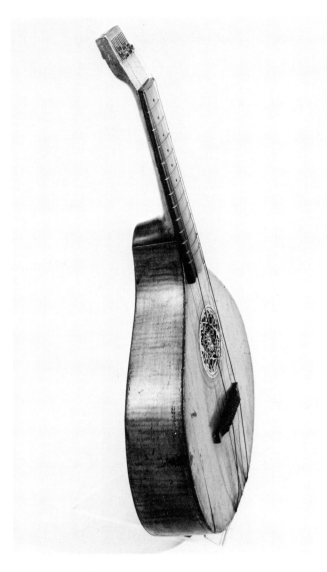

203. ENGLISH GUITAR

Simpson, London

late 18th century

This is a kind of cittern, but is known by the name given above thanks to its extraordinary popularity in England in the second half of the 18th century. At that time its use was restricted to what one standard book succinctly summarizes as "feminine amateurs". In place of the traditional pegs in a pegbox or peg disc these instruments use a mechanical "watchkey-screw" tuning mechanism. Most such tuning boxes are surmounted by a decorative wooden hook (No. 205) corresponding to scroll or carved head atop the tuning means on various other string instruments, but that piece is missing in this instance. The instrument is marked in two places on the exterior with the incised name "Simpson", a well-known London dealer and sometime maker. The shallow flat back is characteristic of most citterns.

Rose of stamped brass. Overall L 62.9 cm. body W 29.9 cm. body D 7.0 cm. The Montreal Museum of Fine Arts, 957.Dv.4.

204. BELL CITTERN

Anonymous, Hamburg

Dated 1714

Like Joachim Tielke, the bell-shaped cittern is a Hamburg native, and there are eight in existence signed by that outstanding master, all made before 1695. This one is unsigned, but has both date and "Hamburg" on its label, suggesting, of course, that it might well have been made by a Tielke pupil. It is longer than all but one Tielke bell cittern, and its body is considerably longer in proportion to its overall length than any of Tielke's. Five double courses are more common than the six of this instrument.

Three roses, metal frets, ivory and ebony pattern around edge of belly and fingerboard. Overall L 70.0 cm. Body L ca 33.0 cm. Body W 30.0 cm. Musikhistorisk Museet og Carl Claudius' Samling, Copenhagen, C-29.

205. KEYED ENGLISH GUITAR

Longman & Broderip, London

This instrument is much like No. 203, but has the decorative hook above its pegbox. More important, it has been built to include an integral key mechanism, a wonderfully simple device that produces the sound from each string not by plucking or even bowing, but by tapping, accomplished by light hammers from within. A keybox is mounted on the edge of the belly with six keys, one for each string, and these are attached to levers and hammers inside the soundbox. The small hammers rise through the six holes incorporated in the rose. This improvement, if indeed it was that, enjoyed a short vogue, which also saw the invention of a wholly self-contained keybox that could be added to an English guitar not equipped with the built-in variety.

Four double and two single courses. Collection of Musical Instruments of Dorothy and Robert Rosenbaum, Scarsdale, 251.

206. HARP-LUTE GUITAR

Harley, London

Early 19th century

This hybrid was yet another invention born of the tantalizing dream of creating a satisfying means of simple, musical self-expression, that (a) would require little of that drudgery known as practising, (b) would be fairly cheap to manufacture under the new methods of mass production, and (c) would have a tonal quality that would be seen as an improvement in some way over the basic cittern or guitar sound. The search continues in our own day and has even accelerated, thanks to transistors and electronics.

L 91.0 cm. Body L 43.0 cm. Body W 37.6 cm. Collection of Musical Instruments of Dorothy and Robert Rosenbaum, Scarsdale, 253.

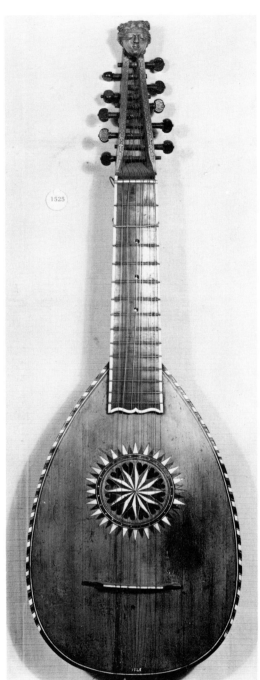
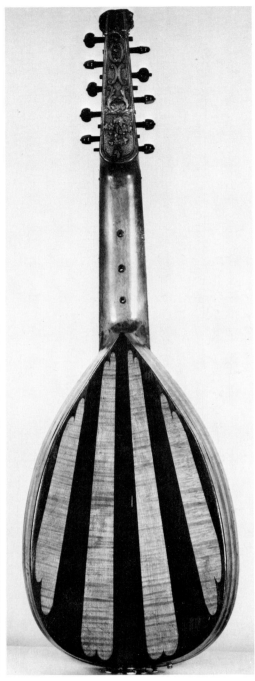

207. CITTERN

Gerald J. Delaplancque, Lille (. . .1760-1790. . .)

dated 1764

This French cittern offers an interesting contrast with its somewhat mechanized contemporaries, Nos. 203 and 205. There are four single courses and above these three double courses, tuned *e, a, d', e', a'-a', c#''-c#'', e''-e''*. The traditional carved head and pegbox, the latter nicely carved on its back surface, give it the look of an earlier

instrument and certainly a fine quality. The neck is drilled to permit use of a *capotasto* to raise pitch a minor third, a perfect fourth, or a perfect fifth. Delaplancque made violins and lutes as well as various types of citterns, and this instrument reflects that traditional skill.

Label: *Gerald J. Delaplancque, Luthier au Marche aux Poulets, a Lille 1764.*

Ebony and ivory rose with star design, belly has ebony edging inlaid with ivory. Overall L 86.0 cm. W 27.0 cm. Musée Instrumental, Brussels, 1525.

208. HARP

Anonymous, French

Late 18th century

This harp is said to have belonged to the Comtesse de Puissieux, lady in waiting to Marie Antoinette. It is very similar to harps by the celebrated Nadermann and Cousineau firms of Paris about this time, but there is no marking on it whatever. The exposed wood is mahogany, which contrasts beautifully with the gilded portions. There are the usual seven pedals.

Overall H 165.4 cm. D 92.7 cm. The Montreal Museum of Fine Arts, 957.Df.3.

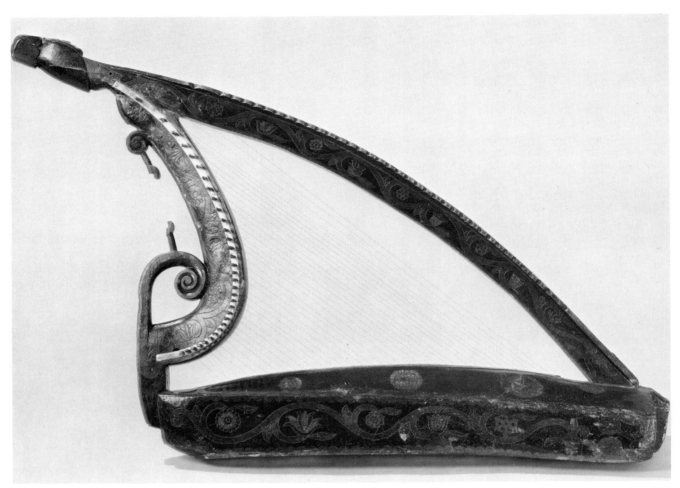

209. CLARSECH (IRISH HARP)

John Kelly

Dated 1734

This large Irish minstrel harp has a sound box hollowed out of a solid block of bog oak. According to its inscription, it was made by John Kelly for the Reverend Charles Bunworth, of the town of Baltdaniel, who was rector of Buttevant, County Cork. Bunworth was very well known as an authority on Irish music and also as a performer on the Irish harp. He presided from 1730 to 1750 over the annual conventions of the Bards of Ireland. Full details of this harp's ornamentation and stringing are found in Bessaraboff.

Harps of this type were strung with metal strings which were plucked with the fingernails, ''grown long expecially for this purpose'', according to Bessaraboff. When the instrument came into the possession of Canon Galpin (from whom it passed eventually to the Boston museum), it had been restrung with gut strings out of concern that the frame would no longer support the greater tension of steel strings. Originally it was painted green, red, and white, but the green paint has oxidized to its present black colour.

Overall H 169.0 cm. Strings' vibrating L 8.5 cm. to 112.0 cm. Museum of Fine Arts, Boston, 17.1787.

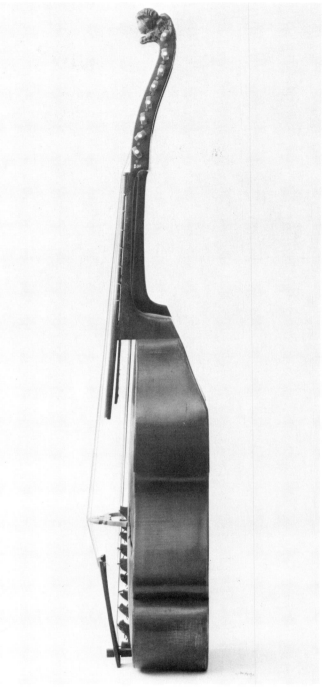

210. BARYTON

Anonymous, Austrian

18th century

This instrument is a variety of bass *viola d'amore* Nos. 147 and 148), but differs by having frets and by the fact that the wire sympathetic strings pass up the back of the neck where they can be plucked by the left thumb. This particular instrument has five gut strings which are bowed and twelve sympathetic strings. The principal importance of the baryton stems from the fact that Joseph Haydn's patron-employer, Prince Esterhazy, was an accomplished player of the difficult instrument, with the result that Haydn wrote 175 compositions for it in various combinations with and without other instruments. These works are of sufficient interest to cause reproductions of the baryton to be made and sold once again today.

Overall H 130.0 cm. Body H 63.0 cm. Body W 36.0 cm. Musikhistorisk Museet og Carl Claudius' Samling, Copenhagen, D-10.

211. FORTEPIANO ACTION

Bartolommeo Cristofori, Florence (1655-1731)

ca 1725

Only a few specialists have known of the existence of this complete fortepiano action by Cristofori, long owned by the Kraus family who until early in this century also owned the fortepiano by Cristofori now in the Leipzig Musik-instrumenten Museum, no. 212 in *The Look of Music*. In all there are only three Cristofori fortepianos that survive; this one from Leipzig, a newly discovered one in Rome, and the earliest of all, which is dated 1720 and has had parts of its action replaced, in the Metropolitan Museum of Art in New York City. With this separate action, displayed in *The Look of Music* for the first time, it may be said that three and one half Cristofori fortepianos survive.

Cristofori himself was a harpsichord maker in the employ of Prince Ferdinand dei Medici at a time when all of Europe had been dazzled by the astonishing artistry of Pantaleon Hebenstreit, a touring virtuoso dulcimer-player. Others as well as Cristofori realized immediately how attractive would be a new instrument that employed a keyboard to strike the strings of an oversized dulcimer like Hebenstreit's. Had Christofori not managed to be first with such a device, someone else would surely have achieved it in his place, but in all likelihood not with the genius that made Cristofori's invention so simple and yet so efficient that it remained essentially unimproved for nearly 100 years.

Overall L 80.0 cm. overall D 41.7 cm. H 15.0 cm. Compass C-c'''.
Private collection, Vancouver.

212. FORTEPIANO

Bartolommeo Cristofori, Florence (1655-1731)

dated 1726

The piano still occupies such a prominent place in the world of music today that this instrument will be, for many people, the highlight of *The Look of Music.*

Think of the problems that faced that Italian harpsichord maker, who wished to connect a keyboard to a striking mechanism and also to improve upon the long existent clavichord by making it strike either hard or softly: it should be able to sustain the sound to some degree for as long as desired, or to stop it at once. He also wanted a mechanism that would be ready to strike again immediately for fast repeated notes of the same pitch. And — after all that — to do this *silently.*

The photograph reproduced here is virtually the first to be published that show this instrument minus its 19th century outer case, in which it was mounted until very recently. The actual inscription on the name board is: BARTHOLOMAVS DE CHRISTOPHORIS PATAVINVS INVENTOR FACIEBAT FLORENTIAE MDCCXXVI.

Principal wood: cypress. Compass C to c'''. Overall L 239.0 cm. Overall W 82.0 cm. Overall H on replacement legs, 83.0 cm. Musikinstrumenten-Museum der Karl-Marx-Universität, Leipzig, 212.

213. FORTEPIANO

Johann Andreas Stein, Augsburg (1728-1792)

Dated 1783

In October 1777, Mozart wrote to his father, "This time I shall begin at once with Stein's pianofortes . . . I much prefer Stein's, for they damp ever so much better than the Regensburg instruments. When I strike hard, I can keep my finger on the note or raise it, but the second ceases the moment I have produced it. In whatever way I touch the keys, the tone is always even. It never jars, it is never stronger or weaker or entirely absent; in a word, it is always even . . . His instruments have this special advantage over others that they are made with escape action. Only one maker in a hundred bothers about this. But without an escapement it is impossible to avoid jangling and vibration after the note is struck. When you touch the keys, the hammers fall back again the moment after they have struck the strings, whether you hold down the keys or release them.

The name board inscription reads, *"JEAN ANDRE STEIN/ faiseur d''orgues, des Clavecins, / et Organiste a la l'Eglise des / Minorittes, a Augsburg. / 17 (handwritten) 83."*

Case walnut veneer on pine core. Two knee levers: damper register and moderator. L overall 216.0 cm. W 98.0 cm including moldings. Compass FF-f'''. Museum of Fine Arts, Boston, 1977.63.

214. GRAND PIANO

Pascal Taskin, Paris (1723-1793)

ca 1780

Taskin is one of the last great French harpsichord makers. He is known as much for the *ravalement* (overall enlargement and addition of further stops) he performed on earlier harpsichords by other makers (including Ruckers: see No. 153) as for his own fine harpsichords and pianofortes. It is believed that he made counterfeit Ruckers instruments, as well.

This grand piano retains most details of Cristofori's mechanism. It is not signed but has one of Taskin's printed professional cards pasted inside, which reads, *"PASCAL TASKIN, Facteur / de Clavecins & Garde des Instruments / de Musique du Roi, Elève & Succes / seur M. Blanchet, rue de la / Verrerie, vis-a-vis S. Merry. / A PARIS."* The case is gessoed and painted with classical scenes over a blue background. The stand is in Louis XIV style, covered with carved gesso, and is entirely gilt.

Overall L 183.5, cm. W 89.5 cm. H of case only 24.8 cm. Compass FF-f'''. Yale University, Collection of Musical Instruments, New Haven, 327.

215. GRAND PIANO

Errico Gustadt, Naples

Dated 1798

This handsome piano is externally more like Stein (No. 213) or the Viennese makers of the period than Taskin, whose piano case is much like the massive harpsichords he also made. Below the keyboard under the left front is a knee lever that controls the dampers on the strings. Of the 61 pitches, the lower 40 are double strung. The mechanism is a German action with escapement and no backcheck, much restored.

Overall L 215.3 cm. W 96.7 cm. H 86.3 cm. with lid closed. Compass FF-f'''. The Metropolitan Museum of Art, New York, 67.51.

216. SQUARE PIANO

Johannes Zumpe, London

Dated 1768

The earliest surviving square piano by Zumpe is dated 1766 and is in the Broadwood Collection, London. Zumpe himself immigrated to England in 1760 after learning piano-making in the celbrated Silbermann workshop in Germany, and joined the London firm of the Swiss harpsichord maker Burkat Shudi. Zumpe made only square pianos and his instruments became the rage of London. In 1768, in fact, the world's first piano recital was given in London by Johann Christian Bach, son of Johann Sebastian, playing a Zumpe square. There cannot have been many times when a square piano was used on the concert stage, for its design was a compromise intended to save space in the home. The nameboard is inscribed, *"JOHANNES ZUMPE LONDINI FECIT 1768, Princess Street Hanover Square."* There are hand-controlled stops at the left end of the wrestplank.

L 127.0 cm. Compass GG-f'''. Royal Ontario Museum, Toronto, 920.58.

217. SQUARE PIANO

Joseph Kirckman, London

Dated 1796

As in the preceding square by Zumpe, from whose action Kirkman's is derived, there are two hand stops, each controlling a damper that affects either the lower half or upper half of the keys. Kirkman himself was of the third generation of this important Alsatian family of London harpsichord makers. The inscription on the nameboard reads, *"JOSEPHUS KIRCKMAN FECIT LONDINI 1796 / No. 19 Broad Street, Soho"*.

L 154.95 cm. compass FF-f'''. Royal Ontario Museum, Toronto, 913.4.99.

218. GRAND PIANO

John Broadwood & Sons, London

ca 1813

Kelowna, B.C., was the home of this piano until recent years; it belonged to a family whose ancestors had brought it around the Horn. In pencil on the back of its nameboard is the presumed serial number 6995, which leads one to believe that this must be slightly earlier than Number 7362, which John Broadwood had sent to Beethoven in Vienna in 1816. The inscription on the nameboard reads, *"JOHN BROADWOOD & SONS / Makers to His Majesty and the Princesses / Great Pultney Street, LONDON, Golden Square."*

Overall L 248.0 cm. W 113.0 cm. H 90.0 cm with lid closed. Compass FF-f'''. Private Collection, Vancouver.

The Romantic 1825 1900

The 19th century was one of the great periods of invention, feverish experimentation, and mechanical advance. We may take pride in the great scientific and technological achievements of our own century, but in musical instruments at least, the 20th century has brought few major improvements, particularly of the sort that are audible or visible rather than felt by the player.

The trombone is one of the truly great musical instruments, with an uncommonly beautiful tone full of nobility and power. It has retained the same form for nearly five hundred years, including its ingenious double-telescoping slide mechanism which enables the player to fill in the pitches between the basic "bugle series". Today's trombones look like Renaissance trombones except for the gradual change in bell shape from long cone to wide flare. The trombone slide makes possible minute adjustments in pitch from key to key, a subtlety of intonation that most of us can readily hear but which only the violin family shares the ability to produce. All other instruments today - the piano, guitar, trumpet, and every woodwind, for example - are designed to play more than half their pitches out of tune, a compromise our ears have learned to tolerate. Until the beginning of the 19th century, the trumpet and horn had no reliable mechanism for producing a scale. In order to produce even the basic "bugle series" in various keys, players had to carry around extra lengths of tubing. For this reason, several of the horns in this exhibition have up to nine or ten additional "crooks" to plug in at one place or another. Pre-19th century trumpets played either in the lower register (restricted to the bugle's limited series of pitches) or in the extremely high range where the available pitches lie closer together. (This limitation prompted the gorgeous, high trumpet parts in some Baroque music.) Valves eventually proved to be the best solution, but the 19th century saw endless experimentation: for example, with simple keys covering holes along the tube (Nos. 200, 283, 286, and 276) and with adaptations of the trombone slide to trumpets (No. 266).

It was most likely Heinrich Stölzel who, in 1815, invented the first valve that worked (No. 263). Other valve types and shapes followed in quick succession (Nos. 267, 269, 274, and 275). Even after valves were introduced, other solutions were tried: one example was the *cor omnitonique* (Nos. 264, 265) invented by Charles Sax (Adolphe's father). Eventually the rotary valve (No. 270), invented by Joseph Riedl of Vienna, and the piston valve in the form devised by François Perinet, won out, and one or the other is used today on all brass instruments except trombones. Strangely enough, until the 19th century, there was no such thing as a "tuba", no real brass bass. That need was met by the Renaissance serpent until well into the 19th century, and later by such improved "serpents" as the Russian bassoon (No. 286) and the chromatic bass horn (No. 283). By 1835, the tuba made its appearance, and No. 290 is one of the first built by Johann Gottfried Moritz, its inventor.

179

Simple keys and various "forked" fingerings had long made chromatic passages possible for woodwinds, but with the appearance of the larger fingerholes needed to produce more sound and with increasing technical demands from composers, better mechanisms were required. Two different bassoon key systems appeared early in the 19th century, each accompanied by changes in bore dimensions and proportions. Jean-Nicholas Savary was the son of a Parisian instrument maker and so stamped his own instruments "Savary jeune"; he was an outstanding player as well. His brilliant improvements were executed with a rare degree of beautiful workmanship and his instruments were as highly prized then as a performance instrument as they are by collectors today (Nos. 254 & 255). At precisely the same time in Germany, the bassoonist Karl Almenräder combined recent acoustical research and brilliant experiments of his own devising to produce an improved bassoon that was at first stamped with the name of the firm for which he then worked: B. Schott fils, Mainz (No. 257). In 1831, however, Almenräder went into partnership in the nearby village of Biebrich with 19 year-old Johann Adam Heckel, who had just completed his apprenticeship and had apparently already showed such inventiveness and skill that he caught the eye of the older man. Their firm, eventually "Heckel, Biebrich", continues to flourish today and makes the bassoon used by virtually all professionals around the world. The entire workshop is about the size of a modest suburban home.

To this day, oboes also exist in two competing models, again the French vs. the German-Austrian. The latter has a warmer, more reedy sound and retains at least a trace of the bulbous turnings of 18th century oboes. Characteristic forms are seen in Nos. 172, 174, 176, 228 and 229. The fathers of the French oboe, the choice of almost everyone today, were Christophe Delusse (No. 175), Henri Brod (Nos. 230 and 233) and Guillaume Triébert and his sons Frederic and Charles (Nos. 231, 232, 234, and 235). An interesting lineage was established in French oboe making. Delusse's tools were bought after his death by the young virtuoso player, Brod, who seems likely to have worked briefly with Guillaume Triébert, an immigrant from Germany. Their considerable achievements in improving the oboe were furthered by the Triébert sons, then continued by their foreman, François Lorée, whose name is found today on the instrument used by most professional players.

The most important figure in 19th century instrument design was unquestionably Theobald Boehm. The son of an eminent goldsmith, Boehm was born, lived in, made flutes in, and died in the same house in Munich, No. 20 Altheimer Eck, which still stands. Boehm was also a virtuoso flutist, first in the Munich opera orchestra and then, while still young, as a touring recitalist in Europe. The distinguished scholar Philip Bate has described Boehm's genius very well: "One is tempted to say that the position of Boehm is unique in musical instrument history. Cases are known where *dynasties* of *artiste-*

ouvriers have entirely remodelled an instrument-as the oboe in the hands of the Triébert family, or the bassoon with the Heckels - but no other man is known to have started his playing life with an instrument unmechanised save for one primitive key, and to have left it as one of the most perfect and efficient of all.'' Certain features of Boehm's key system were adapted to the clarinet by the gifted craftsman August Buffet of Paris (No. 242). Today we still say (mistakenly) that the clarinet uses the "Boehm system". However, the Buffet name lives on, generations later, as the most prestigious firm making clarinets today.

Adolphe Sax (also the son of an instrument maker) is another genius whose influence has obviously transformed 20th century music. It is quite true that his best known invention - one of the very few, new 19th century instruments of lasting importance - has yet to find a regular seat in the symphony orchestra, nor is it used that often in 20th century orchestral works. On the other hand, the saxophone is required in a number of major chamber works of this century. It also has a large, if predictably uneven, solo literature by well-known composers and continues to be one of the principal voices in jazz, rock, and concert bands as well as a popular instrument in schools. One no longer hears the saxophone dismissed as a fad. To have conceived and perfected such a widely loved, new instrument was no small achievement, and 140 years later there have been few improvements on Sax's original conception (Nos. 252 & 253). The tireless but impecunious inventor also produced an entire family of saxhorns (Nos. 287-289) that were more popular than the saxophone at one time. He was the first to design a dependable, even-toned bass clarinet more than 100 years after that logical idea was first attempted. While seeking to improve the design of an existing instrument, Sax created one of the most bizarre but unforgettable forms that has ever been devised. His multi-belled cornet (Sax also applied the idea to the trombone) has been adopted as a logo for "The Look of Music".

The remaining milestones in 19th century instrument-making have to do with the piano, and not with individual craftsmen but with firms, with merchandising techniques, patent litigation, and mass production. A small piano for the ordinary home was first provided by the late 18th century "square piano" (Nos. 216, 217, and 303) and later by the "abominable" upright. Public demand for pianos was greater than for any other instrument in history, and this plus the difficulty of transporting them caused pianos to be made in nearly every city and in everything from multi-storied factories to backyard work-shops. The extensive yearly lists of patents granted to piano makers and tinkerers make it uncertain who invented what and who simply won the race to the courthouse. Also, during the 19th century, specialist-firms came into exis-tence, supplying only hammers, keys, dampers, and other single parts, more cheaply than they could be make by self-sufficient firms, which consequently took on the function of assembly. At that point, the piano had become the product of too many minds and hands, and the age of the artist-craftsman was over.

There are eleven pre-1860 pianos (plus the Cristofori action) in our exhibition. It seems likely that all were made by individual craftsmen or by workers operating directly under the master's eye. The great Steinway (No. 304) was produced within four years of that firm's founding in New York City and was built by newly arrived German immigrants. The final instrument to be included in this exhibition is a square piano (No. 305) made by the firm of Heintzmann Limited, Ontario. That venerable firm still produces the finest piano made in Canada.

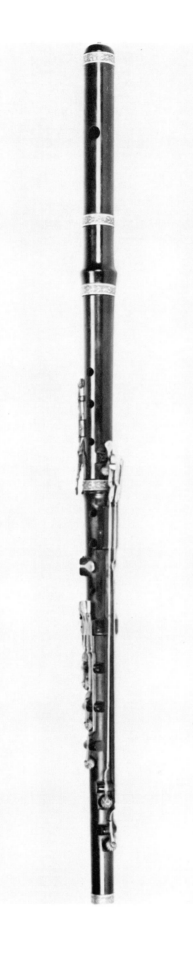

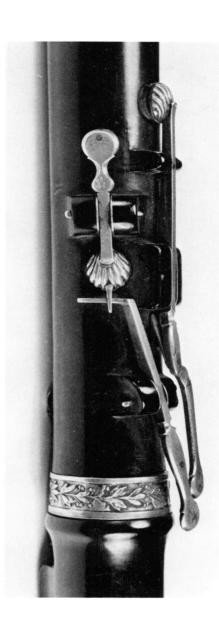

219. FLUTE IN C

Stephan Koch, Vienna (1772-1828)

ca 1825

This maker is one of the finest of any era, in my opinion. His skill in actual design, then in its execution in both wood and metal has very seldom been equalled, the small details being quite as remarkable as the large. His flutes are no less beautiful than his oboes, often descending as here to low a or even, in four examples known to me, to g. The lower keys are of the "plug" type, padless pewter discs that close upon metal seats attached to the wood tube. As Philip Bate has rightly observed, however, "At no time can these instruments have been very efficient. The beauty of their workmanship is beyond question, but with only long simple levers to span such long distances, whip and backlash must have made airtight closing a matter of uncertainty."

Rosewood, with silver mounts and silver-shell flaps. Four sections (head joint, tuning barrel, upper joint, and long lower joint to a). L 78.6 cm. Bate Collection, Oxford, 119.

220. FLUTE IN C

Theobald Boehm, Munich (1794-1881)

circa 1829

This is the standard flute—not nearly as grand or "advanced" as Stephan Koch's—as made by Boehm prior to his first important new design of 1832. Eight-keyed flutes similar to this (but without post and axles key mounts) by Heinrich Grenser and F.G.A. Kirst, for example, are also known. With its clean, well-executed design, this nine-keyed flute shows the jeweller-goldsmith training of Boehm's youth, and is also the plain, no-nonsense instrument of a working professional flautist. For an overall appreciation of Boehm's importance, see the introductory remarks to the instruments of the Romantic Period as well as the comments on the four flutes which follow.

Cocuswood with silver mounts and nine silver keys. Four sections (head joint, tuning barrel, main joint, foot joint). L 67.0 cm. The Library of Congress, Washington, D.C., 975.

221. FLUTE IN C

Theobald Boehm, Munich (1794-1881)

1832 model

In this, his first model with revolutionary changes, Boehm kept the inverse conical bore that had been introduced by the Hotteterres more than 150 years earlier, but enlarged the tone holes for a bigger sound and relocated them to their acoustically correct ("in tune") position, then devised a mechanism by which the fingers could reach them comfortably. This latter was done by the use of plates and rings (which closed a distant hole in addition to the hole being closed by the finger tip) and by the use of rods on pivots that transferred finger action over longer distances than was possible with simple levers (without danger of leaking) as, for example, on Stephan Koch's flute, No. 219. This flute by itself, improved in only small ways by others' modifications, might well have been the standard flute into the 20th century but for Boehm's further advances with his 1847 model.

Boxwood with silver mounts and silver keys. Four sections (head joint, tuning barrel, main joint, foot joint). Has Boehm's "crutch," to aid placement of hand in proper position. L 65.8 cm. Bate Collection, Oxford, 166.

222. FLUTE IN C

Theobald Boehm, Munich (1794-1881)

1832 model

Ebony with silver mounts and silver keys. Four sections (head joint, tuning barrel, main joint, foot joint). Does not have the "crutch" seen on No. 221. L 66.9 cm. Rück Collection Germanisches Nationalmuseum, Nürnberg, MIR 327.

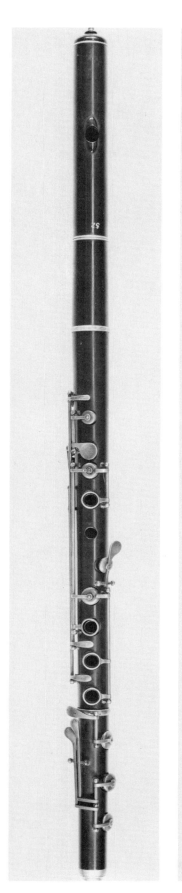

223. FLUTE IN C

Theobald Boehm, Munich (1794-1881)

1847 model

Just as his 1832 model seemed to be gaining widespread acceptance (since professional musicians are among the more adverse to change of all creatures on earth), Boehm applied still more recent acoustical theory and patient, determined experimentation, to produce his 1847 model, in all important respects the flute in use ever since. The 1847 model returned to a mainly cylindrical bore, which the Hotteterres had rejected for a conical bore 150 years earlier, and which was now executed in metal rather than wood.

No. 223 is actually Boehm's 1847 model serial number "1" and therefore a very celebrated instrument. It retains the fingering system of his 1832 model but with a slightly altered layout. It is comprised of a head joint and long one-piece body. It is one of two flutes he ever made with a brass body, the other being no. 2 of the 1847 model.

Brass, with wood tube at embouchure and silver fittings. L 63.5 cm. Bore 1.9 cm. tapering within the head joint to 1.7 cm. at the cork. Library of Congress, Washington, D.C., 652.

224. FLUTE IN C

Theobald Boehm, Munich (1794-1881)

1847 model

No. 224 is an unusual variation by Boehm on his standard 1847 model. Philip Bate describes this instrument in detail in *The Flute*, page 126 of the first edition, and believes it was actually made about 1860. Bate himself found the instrument in a London pawn shop. The close-up shows the unusual mechanism in the area of the B and B^b holes for the left thumb.

Silver, with gold lip plate and gold springs. L 62.0 cm. Bate Colection, Oxford, 150.

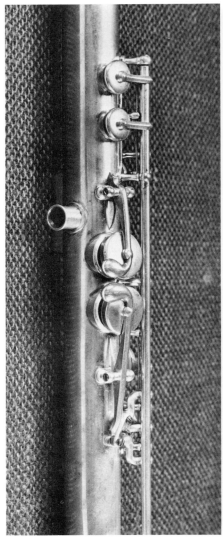

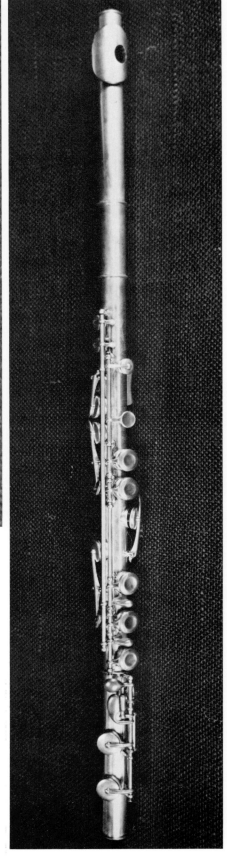

186

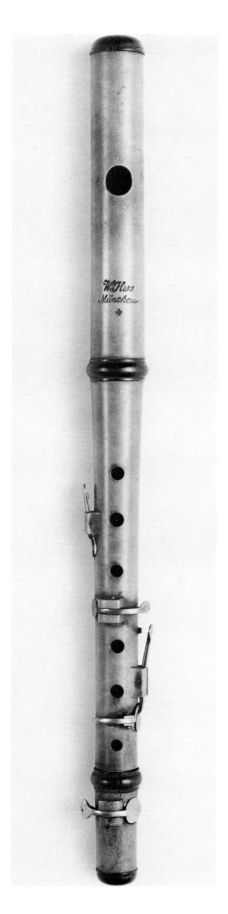

225. PICCOLO IN E♭

W. Hess, Munich (1800-1874)

circa 1840

This small piccolo in e♭'' is by a well-known Munich maker, slightly younger than Boehm. It would be interesting to know what their relationship was, whether he ever worked for or with Boehm, and to what extent he embraced or resisted Boehm's various innovations. Hess apparently apprenticed under Bischoff of Darmstadt, so we know that he was never associated with Boehm in that way, at least. With its simple keys, boxwood body, and horn mounts, we may be quite certain that this instrument was intended for village or military bands.

overall L 30.0 cm. Städt Musikinstrumentensammlung, Munich, 52/38.

226. WALKING-STICK FLUTE

Anonymous

Early 19th century

The 19th century fad for walking sticks with built-in musical instruments flourished particularly in Germany and Austria, with special popularity in Vienna. Not only were flutes and recorders made for double duty as walking sticks, but also oboes, clarinets, bassoons, trumpets, flageolets, and violins! Baines reports one that provides a clarinet at one end and a piccolo at the other. The present specimen is carved to resemble bamboo cane, has six fingerholes, one wooden key, and is decorated with a cord and tassel.

L 82.0 cm. In F. Städt. Musikinstrumentensammlung, Munich, 41/320.

227. WALKING-STICK RECORDER

Stephan Koch, Vienna (1772-1828)

Early 19th century

Stephan Koch was discussed earlier under No. 219. For all his great skill — enough, one would think, to create a waiting list for his flutes and oboes — he also made folk or "popular" instruments; this present example, for instance, and a flageolet in Berlin. Very few walking-stick instruments were made (or at least stamped) by major woodwind makers.

L 83.7 cm. One brass key. Lowest tone g'. Städt. Musikinstrumentensammlung, Munich, 41/397.

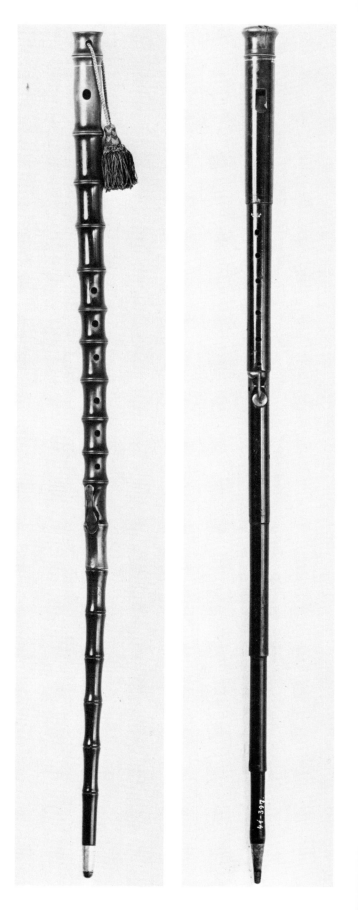

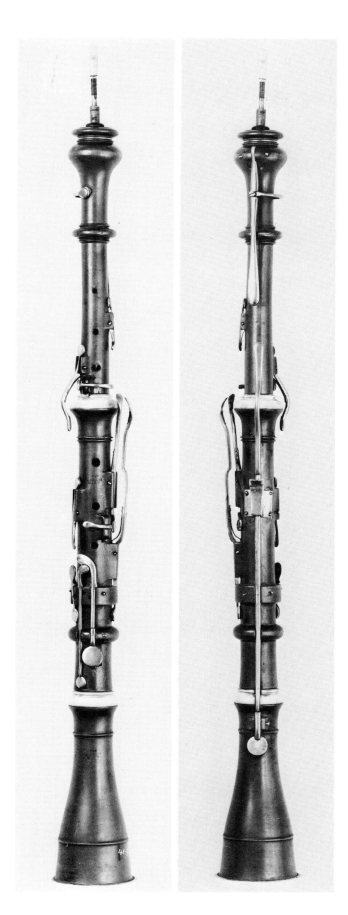

228. OBOE

Stephan Koch, Vienna (1772-1828)

circa 1825

The beautiful craftsmanship and design which are characteristic of this Viennese maker were discussed under No. 219. His oboes are every bit as remarkable as his flutes. Josef Sellner was a distinguished oboist, first in Prague when Weber was the opera director and later in Vienna, and devised several additions to oboe keywork which became known as the "Sellner System". For a short time, at least, Koch was the exclusive maker of that oboe, of which the present specimen is an example. Notice the fact, also seen on the Koch flute, that only integral blocks are used as key mounts, this at a time when many other makers were using metal saddles exclusively. One can see how much the body profile of this instrument owes to Grundmann (Nos. 172 to 174).

It is true, in fact, that neither Sellner's system nor Grundmann's body profile have been altered very much on the standard Central European oboe used to this day.

Boxwood, with ivory mounts. H 54.3 cm. Städt. Musikinstrumentensammlung, Munich, 41/20.

229. OBOE

Wolfgang Küss, Vienna (1779-1834)

circa 1830

This maker is another yet to receive proper recognition. His instruments are handsomely made, if not with quite the extravagance of delicate detail found on many of Koch's. This oboe is also a Sellner model and like Koch's, uses nothing as a key mount but the traditional, integral block and the basic full knobs of the lower joint. On the other hand, I am not enthusiastic about the squat, compressed look of this bell shape which becomes even more bulbous and squashed together on some later Küss oboes.

Ebony, with ivory mounts including thumbrest. 13 silver keys (with 14 touches). H 55.35 cm. Städt. Musikinstrumentensammlung, Munich, 41/316

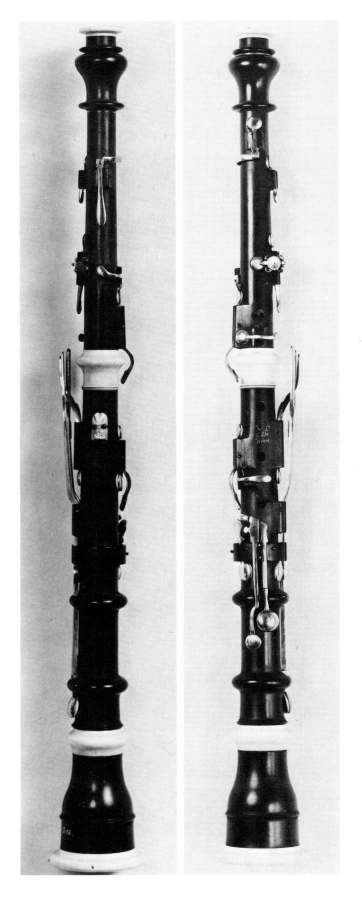

230. OBOE

Henri Brod, Paris (1799-1839)

circa 1835

Young Henri Brod accomplished a remarkable amount in a short lifetime. Accepted in oboe at the Paris Conservatoire at age 12, he was playing second oboe to his former teacher at the Paris Opera at 19. There is reason to think he may have worked with Guillaume Triébert when still quite young and before he bought Delusse's tools to begin making oboes himself about 1835. His instruments are characterized by very slim body lines and delicate keywork, the latter innovative enough to influence the development of the French oboe for a long time to come. If one looks very closely at the present specimen, one can see tiny wheels to reduce the friction of movement of the key springs! This innovation is one that was *not* adopted by other makers. Other Brod instruments in *The Look of Music* are Nos. 233 and 235. The use of screwed-in pillars (posts) for *all* keys was another of his improvements.

Violetwood, with silver mounts and ivory bell ring. L 59.2 cm. Bate Collection, Oxford, 207.

231. OBOE

Guillaume Triébert, Paris (1770-1848)

Circa 1830

This is an early oboe by the German-born father of the French oboe.

Before Henri Brod began making oboes himself, he published an instruction book for oboe in which he identified the 8-keyed oboe by Guillaume Triébert as the best then available. This is an advanced French oboe for its time, but very different from the Sellner oboes we have seen by Koch and Küss of virtually the same date. Despite the more delicate keywork and slimmer body, notice the fact that this instrument is (still) made of boxwood with flat brass keys and ivory mounts, and retains the traditional bulb or ''onion'' at the very top, although this last was soon to disappear permanently from the French oboe.

Boxwood, with ivory mounts. Eight flat brass keys. H 56.2 cm. Bate Collection, Oxford, 219.

232. OBOE

Guillaume Triébert, Paris (1770-1848)

circa 1838

This oboe is not so much later than the previous specimen, but it somehow looks more like a French oboe. The light boxwood colour is gone, as are the ivory mounts and brass keys, and in their place is a dark, slim wood tube without knobs anywhere but at the top, and silver keys all on posts and axles. From this point on, more and more keys are added, but with relatively little change in overall appearance. Triébert's sons, Charles-Louis and Frédéric, took over from their father, the first always more conspicuous as a virtuoso player, while the second remained the experimenter and director of the firm until his death in 1878. By that time, the Triébert oboe had reached a form that has since changed very little to our own day.

Stained boxwood with silver mounts and silver keys. H 56.1 cm. Bate Collection, Oxford, 235.

233. BASS OBOE

Henri Brod, Paris (1799-1839)

This is a very special instrument. The only reference to anything like it is found in Bate's *The Oboe* on page 114 of the third edition, which may well be the same instrument, and I have not seen a twin in any other collection. It looks very much like Brod's well-known *Cor anglais moderne*. The bell is very similar with its lower flange as if to assist it in standing by itself. At the very top above the knob, the metal "spool" can be pulled out as a tuning slide. There are ten brass keys, including a rocker on eb, all of which are finished in a gilt-paint or perhaps "brushed" brass finish that is used on the mounts as well. The gold-coloured metal against the rosewood body is quite garish and unlike anything else I have seen.

Rosewood, with dull-finish gold mounts and 10 keys, all on posts and axles. Three sections plus crook. H 102.0 cm. with crook. 96.7 cm. without crook. Collection of Musical Instruments of Dorothy and Robert Rosenbaum, Scarsdale, 96.

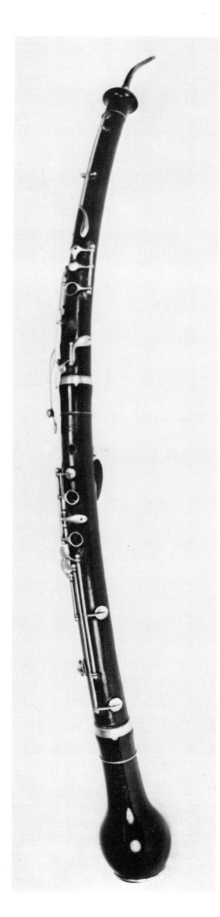

235. BARITONE OBOE in C

Frédéric Triébert, Paris, 1813-1878.

Mid 19th C.

This lovely shape obviously owes much to the similar one by Charles Bizey (No. 96) made more than 100 years earlier. The purpose, of course, was to fold roughly 100 cm. of tube in such a way as to put the finger holes in comfortable positions and to have a reasonably compact and well-balanced shape to hold. This instrument succeeds well in both instances.

Stained boxwood, with German silver mounts. Five sections. H 73.7 cm. Tube L 99.9 cm. Bate Collection, Oxford, 260.

234. ENGLISH HORN

Frédéric (?) Triébert, Paris (1813-1878)

circa 1850

There seems to be no distinguishing mark to help us differentiate between instruments made by father Guillaume or any of his sons. This instrument is a combination of old and new, suggesting the date above, but why was it curved (requiring leather wrapping and other complicated methods) when Jakob Grundmann, for one, has made simpler, angular-form English horns as early as 1791? One would think that the leather-bound curved tube, like the basset horn, would have died during the 18th century. Other makers also continued to make English horns in this way, however, placing German silver ring-system keys on the leather-wrapped curved body.

Both horn and German silver mounts. H 77.0 cm. Bate Collection, Oxford, 252.

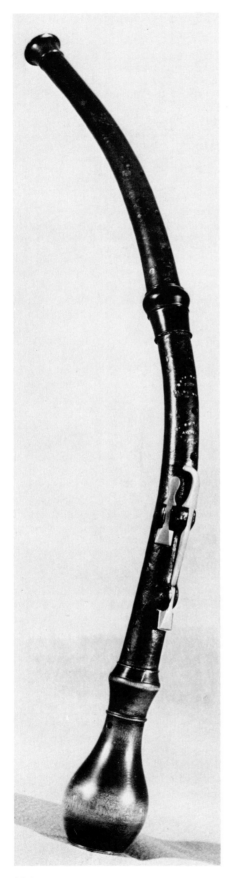

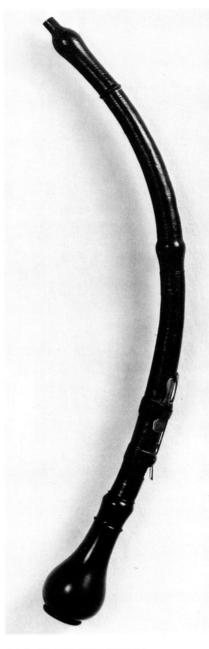

237. ENGLISH HORN

P. Piana, Milan

Early 19th century?

In this case, we know the initial of the first name (see No. 236), but can only guess as to the maker's dates. It is appalling how little activity or interest there is in Italy in instruments in general, especially winds, with the result that museums are poorly maintained or "closed temporarily", catalogues are atrocious if they exist at all (always excepting Vinicio Gai's fine example), and all mail goes unanswered. This particular maker seems to be less of a specialist than Fornari and is represented by a wide assortment of woodwinds in modern collections. The disproportionately large number of English horns of Italian origin would seem to result from the frequency with which the instrument occurs in Italian opera orchestras, but may also stem from more common use in bands than occurred in other parts of Europe; this is pure conjecture, however.

L along outside of curve 76.8 cm., not including crook. Two brass keys. Three sections not including crook. *Stadt. Musikinstrumentensammlung, Munich, 42/210.*

236. ENGLISH HORN

Fornari, Venice (. . .1792-1832. . .)

Dated 1795

We do not even know the first name of this interesting Italian maker, who specialized in oboes and English horns and made a number of especially beautiful ones. The design of the flaps here employs a shape he used a great deal, and shows his individuality with so simple a form as the square flap. This is his own variation that I have not seen used by others, and he uses it with brass, silver, and ivory keys. Here again on this English horn is a leather-wrapped curved body, but at a much earlier date than prompted the comments on the preceding instrument.

Tube covered with black leather with black horn mounts. Maple bell. Two brass keys. There was at least one other, added key, now removed. Three sections not including crook. L. along outside of curve 77.7 cm. Collection of Musical Instruments of Dorothy and Robert Rosenbaum, Scarsdale, 92.

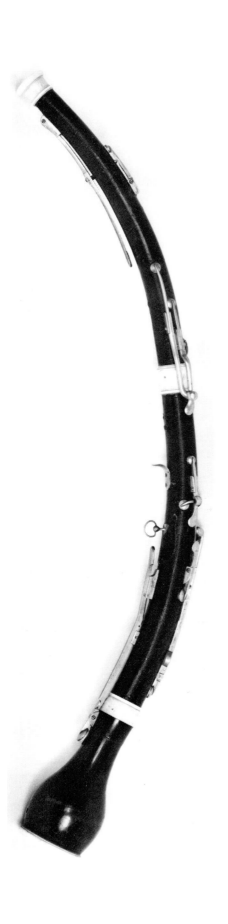

238. ENGLISH HORN

Carl Golde, Dresden (? -1873)

No direct link other than Dresden has been found between Grundmann or August Grenser and Golde, but they seem to represent the first and last generations of a school of woodwind making, especially of oboe types, that was prominent for over a hundred years. Between them came Heinrich Grenser, Floth, Wiesner, and Bormann, and perhaps others. As observed earlier, a disproportionately large number of their instruments found their way to Scandinavia, especially Sweden. The impetus for this migration may have been simply an effective salesman, or there might have been an influx (as yet undocumented) of Dresdener wind players to Scandinavia. No less than August Grenser's second son was an oboist in Stockholm and died there in 1794, but that was before most of the instruments in question were made. At any rate, Carl Golde is a skilled maker in the Dresden mold, and this curved, leather-covered English horn may well be later still than the Triébert example, No. 235.

Black leather covered, with ivory mounts and grenadilla (?) bell. Twelve German-silver keys. L along outside of curve 79.0 cm. Musikmuseet, Stockholm, No. 292.

239. ENGLISH HORN

Johann Heinrich Gottlieb Streitwolf, Gottingen (1779-1837)

This maker is of considerable interest for a number of fresh solutions he found to major problems of design, including the English horn, which he cast in the shape seen here. Another similar example of this model is in the Germanisches Nationalmuseum, Nürnberg. He is further represented in *The Look of Music* by a bass clarinet (No. 248) and a chromatic bass horn (No. 238). He made the full spectrum of woodwinds, all of a high level of craftsmanship.

Eighteen brass keys and brass U-bend at the bottom. Five sections. H 76.5 cm. Institute of Theatre, Music, and Cinematography, Leningrad, 783.

240. HECKELPHONE

Wilhelm Heckel KG, Biebrich (Wilhelm Heckel, 1856-1909)

circa 1920

The importance of the name Heckel has been cited in the introduction to instruments of the Romantic period. Because of the impressive improvements in the bassoon that had been accomplished by his father and himself, 23-year-old Wilhelm Heckel was summoned to Bayreuth in 1879 to be presented to Wagner, who in the course of their talk revealed his conviction that a baritone woodwind was needed which "should combine the character of the oboe with the soft but powerful tone of the Alphorn". Young Heckel addressed himself to the task, succeeding only in 1904, long after Wagner's death, but already in 1905 Richard Strauss gave the new instrument a strong voice in his new opera *Salome,* a lead that a number of other composers soon followed. The Heckelphone has too wide a bore in proportion to its length to be a true oboe, baritone or otherwise, and it is actually a new instrument of oboe ancestry. Philip Bate devotes an excellent, short chapter to it in *The Oboe.* This present specimen is from the Heckel collection itself. The instrument is still made, of course, and is required by every opera house at various times in the normal season. Its sound is extremely beautiful and well worth seeking out in recordings of Strauss and Delius, in particular.

Maple, with German silver mounts. Overall H without crook 117.7 cm. Wilhelm Heckel KG, Biebrich, H-4.

241. CLARINET IN B♭

Eugene Albert, Brussels (1816-1890)

circa 1865

The "Albert System" clarinet has been very much with us into this century, coexisting with and occasionally even preferred to the so-called "Boehm System". A number of New Orleans jazz clarinettists played Albert-system instruments, as did Barney Bigard, the remarkable clarinettist with Duke Ellington's Orchestra and later Louis Armstrong's sextet. This particular specimen is part of a set of C, Bb, and A clarinets that belonged to Henry Lazarus, one of the great English clarinettists (1815-1895), from whom it passed to Frederick Thurston, another outstanding player, who eventually presented it to Philip Bate.

The actual stamp: *E. ALBERT, a BRUXELLES (star). Sole agents S.A. Chappell, 45 New Bond Street, Approved by Mr. Lazarus.*

Cocus, with silver plated mounts and keys. L excluding mouthpiece 57.1 cm. Bate Collection, Oxford, 458.

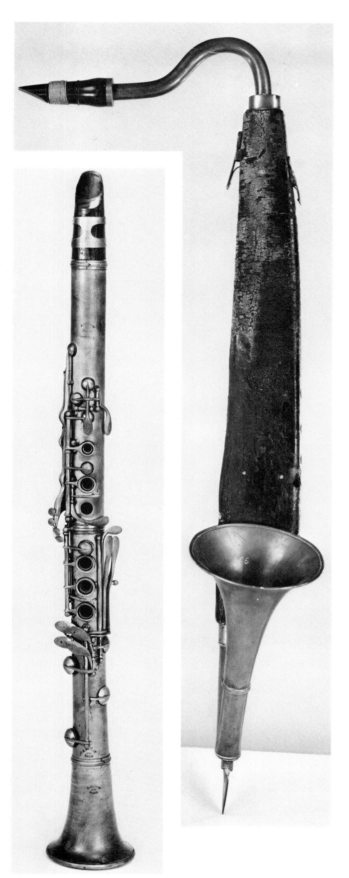

242. CLARINET IN C

Auger Buffet, jeune, Paris (1831-1885)

The Buffet clarinet has long been the favorite instrument of both professionals and serious younger players, and it seemed appropriate to include an early one in *The Look of Music* to complete the remarkable study of clarinet development beginning with Denner's *chalumeau*. This instrument is still of boxwood, although grenadilla had become the favoured wood by this time, as had German silver for keys instead of brass. This particular model does not have a separate barrel joint. The key system is that called by Boehm's name, used on virtually all clarinets today.

Actual stamp: *Buffet, A., jne, Paris, breveté.*

Boxwood, with brass mounts and keys. Cocuswood mouthpiece, not original. L. excluding mouthpiece 50.7 cm. Bate Collection, Oxford, 462.

243. BASS CLARINET

Anonymous

circa 1750(?)

The Look of Music displays seven bass clarinets together in a single case, even though the exhibition is otherwise organized chronologically. This seems justified since the bass clarinet did not achieve orchestral status until the Romantic Period and only in the 20th century has it been heard with any frequency. It is a glorious instrument. On at least one occasion, Stravinsky said it was his favourite of all instruments.

This strange first example is similar to four others, the oldest of which seems to have been the one in Berlin, which tragically was lost in World War II. All four had/have a wide body cut from a plank, permitting its fingerholes to be drilled obliquely at considerable distance into its bore that runs along one edge. Neither date, maker, nor country of origin is known of any of the four, but if authentic, the Berlin example would appear to have been the oldest bass clarinet of which we know. The other three would appear to be only slightly younger, perhaps 1750, as given above. One authority has asked if these might not be the *bass de chalumeau,* for which Graupner wrote on several occasions. I myself am uneasy about all of these specimens, the metal portions of which do not seem to be nearly as old as the body pieces may be.

Brass bell, bottom piece, neck, and three keys. Overall H 136.0 cm. Musée Instrumental, Brussels, 939.

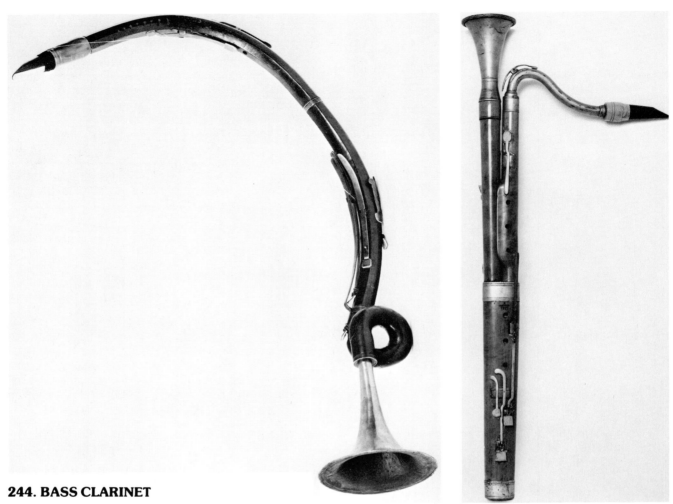

244. BASS CLARINET

Anton Sr. and Michael Mayrhofer, Passau (1706-1774)
(1707-1778)

circa 1760(?)

This instrument may be the oldest bass clarinet in existence. The makers also produced the basset horn (No. 185), using the same stamp which also identifies them as the inventors. This instrument is pitched an octave lower than the standard Bb clarinet, but — like a basset horn — has additional keywork that extends its range downward a major third to BBb, in this case without providing any pitch between D and BBb. Unlike the Mayrhofers' basset horns, the main tube is in two sections. A unique feature is the 360° coil of wooden tube, covered with leather like the main tube sections, which condenses approximately 34.0 cm. of air column into a 12.0 cm.-long section, replacing the *kasten* (the triple-bored block of wood seen on Nos. 186 to 188) of most basset horns. It has a bass-clarinet sound and good intonation. The eminent Rainer Weber repaired damage to the upper end, and also constructed a replacement bell, mouthpiece and barrel.

Maple, covered with brown leather. Seven brass keys, brass bell and mounts. Six sections (mouthpiece, barrel, upper body, lower body, coil, bell.)Air column L ca. 177.0 cm. Bore L 1.58-1.67 cm. Städt. Musik-instrumentensammlung, Munich, 52.50.

245. BASS CLARINET

Heinrich Grenser, Dresden (1764-1813)

Dated 1793

Until very recently this was believed to be the first bass clarinet, dated 1793, but with much confusion about which Grenser's initial was stamped on it. It is certainly Heinrich's and this is the only instrument of 134 known to us on which he stamped the date. His uncle August, obviously impressed with 29-year-old Heinrich's "invention", made one too, dated 1795 and now in Darmstadt. The adoption of the bassoon's form as a solution to the problem of compressing the long tube needed for a bass clarinet was but one of many ideas which were tried and found wanting. Several other ideas and variations on this one are the next examples to be seen. Eventually, it was Adolphe Sax who gave the bass clarinet a straight tube with downturned neck and upturned bell, the form the instrument retains to this day. Unfortunately, *The Look of Music* does not include Sax's bass clarinet, but these seven are all more fascinating to look at than his!

Maple or boxwood, with brass mounts and eight brass keys. 80.4 cm. Air column length circa 190.0 cm. Bore 1.48-1.5 cm. Musikmuseet, Stockholm, 1957-85/28.

246. BASS CLARINET

Nicola Papalini, Chiaravalle

circa 1820

The Mayrhofers, who apparently invented the basset horn and believed they had invented the bass clarinet, are survived by just three of the first and one of the latter, which may have been their entire output. Papalini is represented today by only five serpentine bass clarinets : we know nothing more about him.

This example is in my opinion the earliest of the five. The most striking differences are that this one has a larger diameter bell, has neat wooden pegs that bind the two halves together, has its finger holes numbered (with numbers stamped beside the holes), and has a simpler form of f# key. The bodies of all five are made of two blocks of wood into the surfaces of which are carved the bore channels, one side in mirror-image of the other, exactly as in a cornetto (see No. 14). The exterior is thus reduced to a serpentine design, imitating the bore contour.

Maple, with horn mounts. Five brass keys. Overall H 67.2 cm. Musée Instrumental, Brussels, 940.

247. BASS CLARINET

Nicola Papalini, Chiaravelle

circa 1820

In contrast with the Brussels specimen's maple, this instrument is of pearwood, while the New York example is of cocus and olivewood. This one has the smaller bell diameter in common with the other three, has iron pins that hold the halves together (vs. Brussels' wooden pegs and New York's lack of any), and otherwise resembles No. 246.

I believe this to be the oldest after the Brussels example, followed by Leipzig, Paris and New York respectively. Sharp-eyed readers will note that there are more finger holes than we have fingers! As on the rackett (No. 105) the lower, fleshy portion of the finger (as well as the tip) is used in some cases to cover a hole. The nuisance of this variation may have been the principal reason for Papalini's apparent abandonment for his bass-clarinet design.

Pearwood, with horn mounts. Five brass keys. Overall H. 68.0 cm. Museum of Fine Arts, Boston, 17.1879.

248. BASS CLARINET

Johann Heinrich Gottlieb Streitwolf, Göttingen (1779-1837)

circa 1825

The bassoon shape continued to entice redesigners of the bass clarinet. Heinrich Grenser's apparently worked well enough, even though he never made another after the first, and a number of other makers, even several in the United States, produced workable bass clarinets in this model in the first quarter of the 19th century. This attempt by Streitwolf drew considerable praise when it first appeared, and the fact that at least six survive in various museums would suggest that he made quite a few. Obviously it was a great advantage to have the bass clarinet in such a compact package, especially for marching use, away from the ground and moving knees.

Rosewood, with brass mounts and bell. Nineteen brass keys. Overall H 90.6 cm. Haags Gemeentemuseum, Holland, Ea 135-1950.

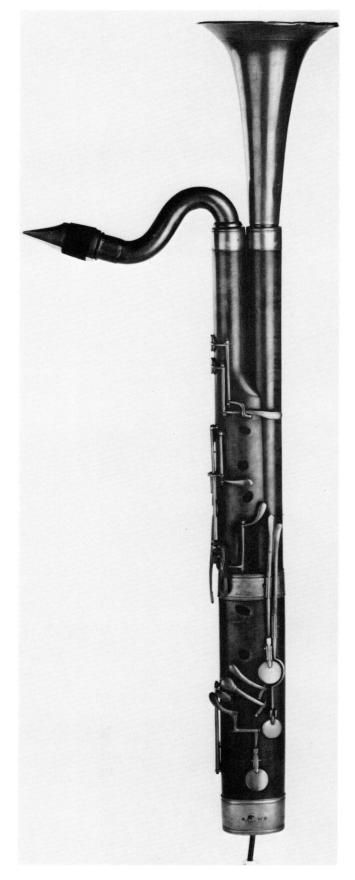

249. BASS CLARINET, THEATRE MODEL

Jean Baptiste Albert, Brussels (? -1918)

circa 1900

This is specifically intended for use in the theatre pit where compactness is the first requisite. It certainly achieves that and is a sturdy instrument as well, though extremely heavy. It is keyed on the Albert System (see No. 241). The body design is, of course, very much derived from the baritone saxophone. Notice how abruptly the bell swells once it leaves the lowest wood section.

Rosewood, with German silver mounts and keys. Overall H 70.7 cm. Collection of Musical Instruments of Dorothy and Robert Rosenbaum, Scarsdale, 147.

250. SOPRANO SAXOPHONE

Adolphe Sax, Paris (1814-1894)

circa 1900

This quartet of saxophones, made by either the inventor himself or the inventor's firm after his death, shows the instrument at several different points of development. Sax's serial numbers are as yet very little help in determining age, and one is therefore dependent on clues such as "Medaille or d'Or 1900" or other endorsements that appear on his instruments. Even his inscribed street addresses change so seldom as to be little assistance in defining year of manufacture. This soprano was made after 1900.

Silver plating over brass body. Silver keys. Serial no. 15946. Overall H 64.0 cm. without mouthpiece. Rück Collection, Germanisches National-museum, Nürnberg, MIR 485.

251. ALTO SAXOPHONE IN E♭

Adolphe Sax, Paris (1814-1894)

circa 1900

This instrument would appear to be the latest of the four, not appreciably different from modern examples.

Brass body and keys, all silver plated. Serial no. 15604. Overall H 64.0 cm. Musikmuseet Stockholm, 1959-60/55.

252. TENOR SAXOPHONE IN B♭

Adolphe Sax, Paris (1814-1894)

This saxophone is incredibly light in weight. It would appear to be the earliest of our quartet, but cannot be dated with certainty.

Inscription: *Nr 17059*
Saxophone tenor in Si b brevete
Adolphe Sax in Paris
Fteur de la Mson Milre de l'Empereur

Overall H. 77.4 cm. Bell dia. 14.8 cm. Musée Instrumental, Brussels, 3765.

253. BARITONE SAXOPHONE IN E♭

Adolphe Sax, Paris (1814-1894)

This baritone would seem slightly later than the tenor. The serial numbers suggest this, too, but are not necessarily a guide to date or relative age. Again, it is remarkable how little saxophones have changed in appearance in nearly 150 years.

Silver plating over brass, now very worn. Serial number 20149. Overall H 103.3 cm. Bell dia. 20.4 cm. Musée Instrumental, Brussels, 3663.

254. BASSOON

Jean-Nicolas Savary, jeune, Paris (1786-1850)

Dated 1825

In the first part of the 19th century, two new and markedly improved bassoons made their appearance, and for more than a century they would be seen as intense rivals; the choice between them involved total commitment. In addition to their different ways of arranging keys, each had gradations in bore shape and in soundhole size and placement that actually produced a quality of tone distinct from the other, especially from one register to the next. To the extent that an expert could be impartial, it seems to have been widely agreed that certain notes or areas of notes were more beautiful on the French bassoon, but the overall similarity of tone quality was far better with the German.

The perfector of the French bassoon made the present instrument. It can be seen at once that he was a superb craftsman and designer whose bassoons, usually stamped with the date, are as beautiful as any ever made.

Maple, with brass mounts and ten flat brass keys. H 128.5 cm. Bate Collection, 325.

255. BASSOON

Jean-Nicolas Savary, jeune, Paris (1786-1850)

Dated 1833

This slightly later bassoon by Savary *jeune* shows a number of advances over the previous example — domed keys and more of them, rack and pinion tuning slides in two places, keys mounted on posts on bedplates as well as on saddles, and more. Again, the excellence of workmanship is unmistakable. Every detail has been lavished with extraordinary care and refinement.

Maple, with brass mounts and 16 domed keys. H 127.0 cm. Bate Collection, Oxford, 315.

256. BASSOON

Frédéric Triébert, Paris (1813-1878)

circa 1850

This bassoon by Guillaume Triébert's son continues the refinement of Savary *jeune's* advances and makes some of its own. This appears to be the instrument illustrated in the 1847 *Methode* of Eugène Jancourt, the celebrated bassoonist and teacher at the Conservatoire, whose preface states, "Several skilful makers in our time have contributed to its improvement; in the first rank, we cite Messiers Savary, Adler, and Frédéric Triébert. The last named, though still young, is destined to develop further these improvements. The care he devotes to the making of keys renders performance easier."

Jancourt and Triébert were to collaborate in further improvements, and eventually Triébert attempted unsuccessfully to adapt Boehm's revolutionary principles to the bassoon. That failure was through no fault of his, and his contributions to both oboe and bassoon development assure his place among the most important makers of any period.

Rosewood wing and other sections of maple, with German silver mounts and 17 keys. H 130.5 cm. Musikmuseet, Stockholm, 1963-64/17.

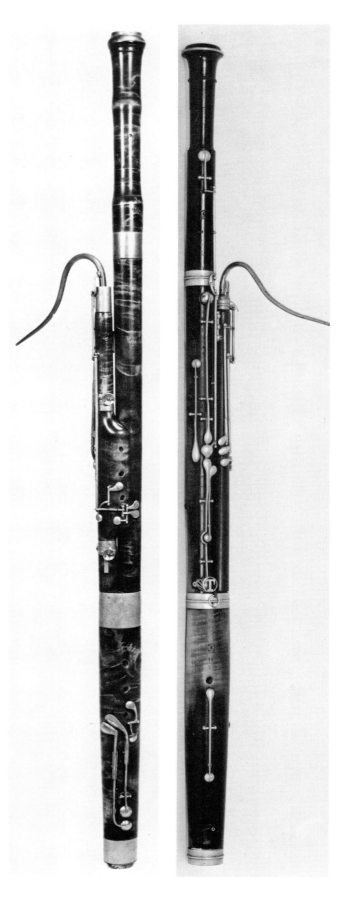

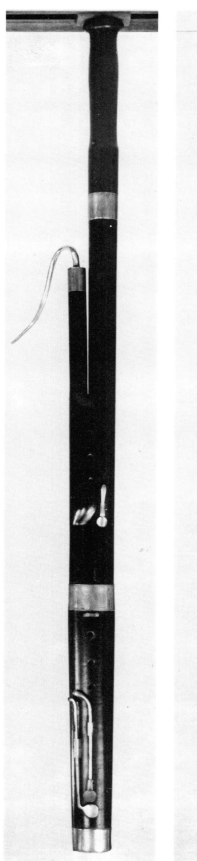

257. BASSOON

B. Schott Fils, Mayence
Karl Almenräder (1786-1843)

circa 1824

The Heckel Company is a 150-year-old family business that continues to produce the finest bassoons made, and their generous cooperation has enriched our exhibition as perhaps no other private company in the world could do. It will not be taken amiss, then, if I say that this bassoon, No. 257, is something of a frustration as well as one of the least attractive instruments in *The Look of Music*. There are but three bassoons still in existence known to me that bear the stamp "B. SCHOTT FILS / A MAYENCE", which is the firm for which Karl Almenräder, the father of the German bassoon, worked originally and which made the bassoons that reflected his first major advances. This particular one from the Heckel Collection is the only one of these that was available to us, and, sadly, the only one in the Heckel Collection. In exterior details, at least, it is no advance over Heinrich Grenser's bassoon, one of which served in fact as Almenräder's "guinea pig" when he began his important experiments. In addition, it has been badly treated at some time and not repaired very well afterward, all of which has done nothing to enhance its appearance today. Even so, it is at least an instrument the making of which Almenräder must have supervised, and its bore may indeed reflect the most important of his initial achievements.

Maple, with brass mounts and ten flat brass keys. H 131.7 cm. Wilhelm Heckel KG, Biebrich, F-10.

258. BASSOON

Heckel, Biebrich
Johann Adam Heckel (1812-1877)

circa 1863

The unpublished catalogue of the Heckel Collection dates this instrument as above, which means that it was made during the lifetime of Johann Adam Heckel and in all likelihood under his supervision.

Heckel and Amlenräder still worked for B. Schott Fils and 17-year-old Heckel was a new employee, just arrived from his birthplace and an apprenticeship in Adorf, still today an area with high concentration on instrument making. Two years later in 1831 they established their own workshop across the Rhine in the village of Biebrich, where the firm has thrived ever since. Until Almenräder's death in 1843 the instruments were stamped and sold by Schott, after which the firm became independent and adopted the stamp "Heckel, Biebrich". Following a number of other Heckels, two successive sons-in-law have directed the business in recent years, but their wives — direct descendants of Johann Adam Heckel — have been in charge of critical operations in the manufacturing process.

Maple, with German silver mounts and 18 keys. H 127.1 cm. Wilhelm Heckel KG, Biebrich, F-26.

205

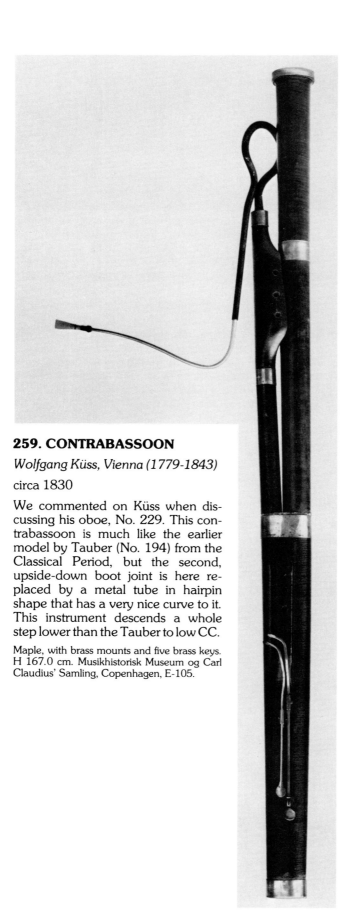

260. CONTRABASSOON

Johann Stehle, Vienna (1808-1862?)

circa 1840

Stehle in all likelihood apprenticed under Küss but in any event took over from him upon the latter's death in 1834. His principal claim to fame is the invention of this all-metal contrabassoon in the thirties, and according to contemporary reports it had three times as much sound as the conventional wooden contrabassoon. It was designed for military bands; the typical German infantry band then included two bassoons and two contras, and its Austrian counterpart used four bassoons and two contras. The great fault of Stehle's metal contra was the complexity of its key system, which made it very difficult to play. Langwill points out that for all the popularity of the contra in Germany and Austria in the first half of the 19th century, it was all but unknown in France and Britain at that time.

Brass, with silver plated or German silver keys. Compass: two octaves. H 146.0 cm. without (missing) bell. Royal Ontario Museum, Toronto, 909.17.15.

259. CONTRABASSOON

Wolfgang Küss, Vienna (1779-1843)

circa 1830

We commented on Küss when discussing his oboe, No. 229. This contrabassoon is much like the earlier model by Tauber (No. 194) from the Classical Period, but the second, upside-down boot joint is here replaced by a metal tube in hairpin shape that has a very nice curve to it. This instrument descends a whole step lower than the Tauber to low CC.

Maple, with brass mounts and five brass keys. H 167.0 cm. Musikhistorisk Museum og Carl Claudius' Samling, Copenhagen, E-105.

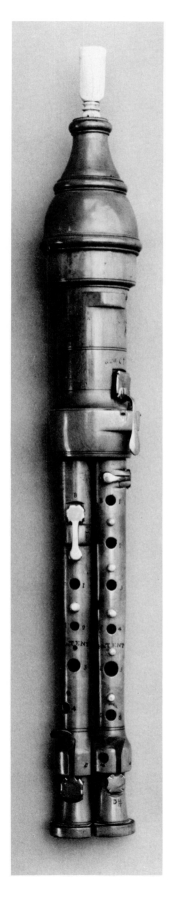

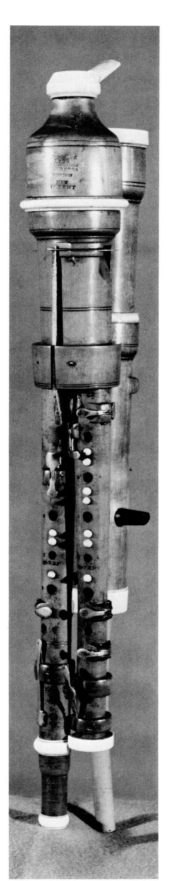

261. DOUBLE FLAGEOLET

William Bainbridge, London (. . .1802-1831)

Flageolets and recorders are similar and have very long histories that need not concern us here. In the early 19th century, this maker took out several patents for various flageolets, including the very popular double shown here (which one could play in parallel thirds or sixths), and the considerably more complex triple No. 262. The ivory buttons between finger holes are intended as a guide to finger placement for the casual or novice player, for whose benefit the pitch names and even the finger-number are stamped beside each hole. The goal was an instrument that the amateur could learn to play quickly and enjoy without very much practice. A similar construction is seen in the traditional Yugoslavian folk instrument, the *dvoynice.* Bainbridge furnishes a cut-off key (the longest one) so that one side of his double instrument can be turned off or added at will in mid-tune. The bulge near the top is a chamber to hold a sponge to absorb condensation lest it interfere with playing.

Boxwood, with ivory buttons and mouthpipe. Six brass keys. H 42.0 cm. School of Music, University of Victoria, 1970-3.

262. TRIPLE FLAGEOLET

Hastrick, London, "late Bainbridge" (. . .1835-1855)

Bainbridge was succeeded upon his death by Hastrick, who in turn was succeeded, it appears, by John Simpson. At any rate, the firm under the several names continued to make single, double, and triple flageolets. The third tube was usually simply a drone, but on this specimen it has both a cut-off key and several other keys for varying the pitch.

Boxwood, with ivory mounts and mouthpipe, and 19 silver keys. H 54.3 cm. Collection of Musical Instruments of Dorothy and Robert Rosenbaum, Scarsdale, 11.

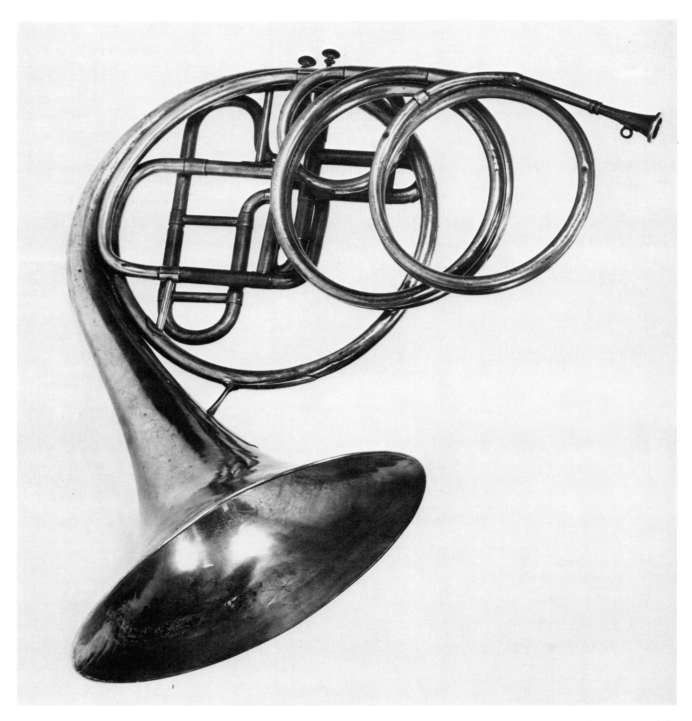

263. HAND HORN WITH TWO ADDED STOLZEL VALVES

Thomas Key, London (. . .1800-1840. . .)

circa 1840

Here may be seen the valves that Stölzel invented in 1815, the great break-through for brass instruments even though it was not Stölzel's but Perinet's version that was eventually adopted as the standard cylindrical valve. The valves here are designed to slip into the tuning slide receivers of the original hand horn, with the first valve lowering pitch a half-step and the second valve a whole step. The two "master crooks" and seven couplers are added between mouthpiece and mouthpipe. The horn earlier belonged to R. Morley-Pegge, who illustrated it in his book, *The Horn,* and pointed out that it is possible to crook this horn in every key from C-alto to G-basso. The mouthpiece is judged to be original.

Dia. of coil 24.0-25.0 cm. Bell dia. 29.0 cm. Bate Collection, Oxford, 62.

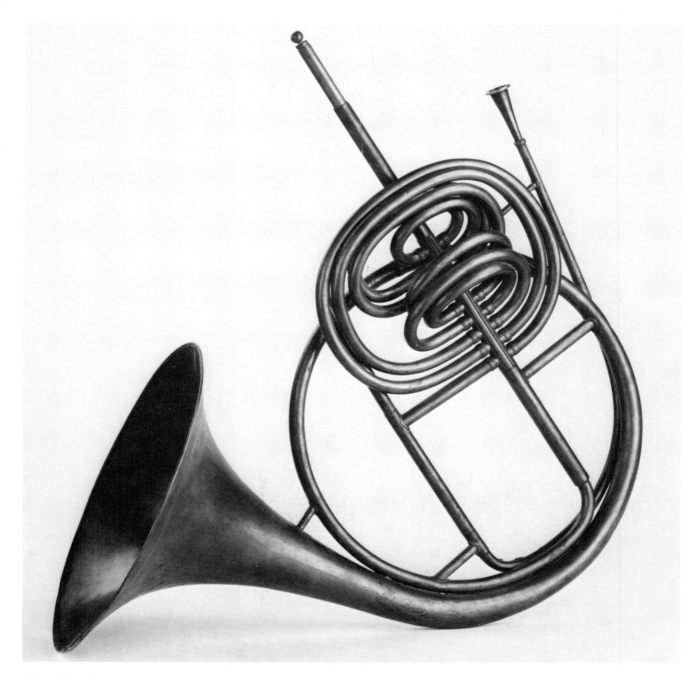

264. COR OMNITONIQUE

Charles Joseph Sax, Brussels (1781-1865)

Adolphe Sax's father was an important instrument maker and gifted inventor who obviously provided a perfect environment for his son's upbringing. The *cor omnitonique* was not Sax *père's* invention, but he made the most successful version of it, as Morley-Pegge said, "commercially and otherwise". It is really a brilliant concept. In this excellent photograph, the rod with the small knob on its end is the adjusting agent. As one pushes it in or pulls it out

to a mark that is calibrated along the edge of that rod, a hole through the rod lines up with adjacent coils of tubing, connecting the selected length to the main column of air of the horn. Nine pitches (keys) are available via the eight possible additions and positions of the rod.

This instrument also includes the prototype of an even greater invention, which only a brass player can appreciate, the water key.

Brass, with silver bell band, mouthpipe, and braces. Overall tube 275.0 cm. Main coil dia. 33.5 cm. Bell dia. 29.5 cm. Haags Gemeentemuseum, Holland, Ea 500-1933.

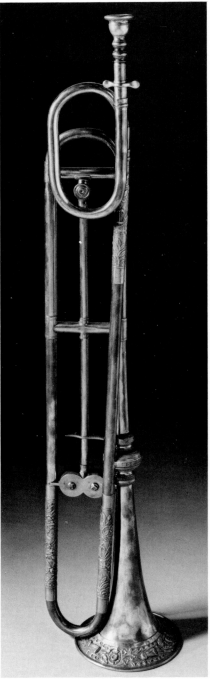

265. COR OMNITONIQUE

Charles Joseph Sax, Brussels (1781-1865)

circa 1826

This example is very similar to No. 264 but has a painted interior bell design, as seen on earlier hand horns in *The Look of Music.* This instrument was in the personal collection of the maker's son, Adolphe, who was eventually obliged to sell it to pay creditors. Fortunately the Conservatoire was able to buy a number of specimens from him at the time for its Musée Instrumental.

Brass. Water key. Dia. main coil 33.8 cm. Musée Instrumental du Conservatoire de Paris, E.757, C586.

266. ENGLISH SLIDE TRUMPET

Charles Pace, London (. . .1830-1850. . .)

Circa 1840

There have been other types of slide trumpets, but in this one, introduced about 1800, there is a U-bend at the upper end toward the mouthpiece which the player can pull toward him, extending the overall length of the tubing. The special feature is a coiled watch spring in a special housing (and a spare in an adjacent housing) attached to a rod to retract the U-bend as soon as it is released by the player. This permits very rapid changes of position from the two or three that are available, back to "closed" position. This device coupled with up to six crooks for insertion between mouthpiece and mouthpipe gave a great deal of flexibility. Difficult as it is to believe, such trumpets were used in the Covent Garden Orchestra, London, and taught at the Kneller Hall School of Music until nearly the end of the 19th century.

Copper, with brass trim. 57.2 without crooks or mouthpiece. Division of Musical Instruments Smithsonian Institution, Washington, D.C. 76.25.

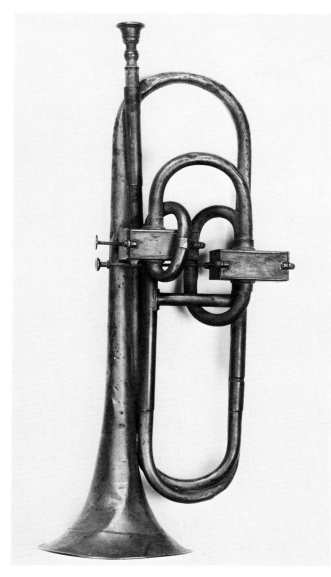

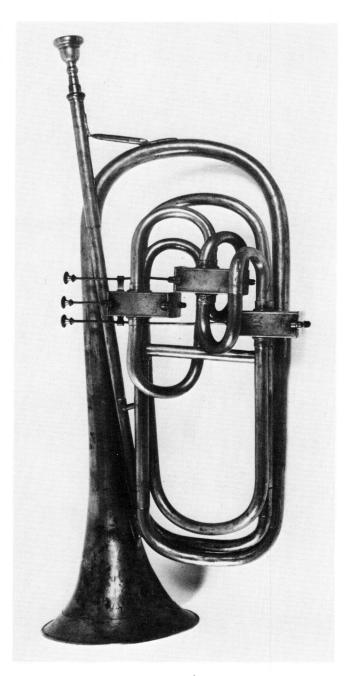

267. VALVE TRUMPET IN E♭

Friedrich Wilhelm Schuster, Karlsruhe (. . .1820-1828. . .)

circa 1825

This is certainly one of the very first valve trumpets in existence and also one of the very few with square valves. (For another, see No. 268.) Heinrich Stölzel patented a valve mechanism in Berlin in 1818, where his invention was seen by a horn player who had originally come from Karlsruhe. That traveller brought a full report back to Schuster, who then proceeded to make them, patent or no patent, until at least 1828, while meanwhile Stölzel had moved on to improved types. These box or square valves work exactly like a piston valve except that the section that moves up and down is a "block" rather than a cylinder. As with most two-valve instruments, the first valve lowers pitch a half-step and the second valves a whole step. (The reverse is standard today.)

L 45.0 cm. Bell dia. 13.2 cm. Rück Collection Germanisches National-museum, Nürnberg, MIR 130.

268. VALVE TRUMPET IN B♭

Friedrich Wilhelm Schuster, Karlsruhe (. . .1820-1828. . .)

circa 1825

This instrument is slightly later than the previous example and was made by the same maker : the same comments apply here. The first valve lowers pitches by a half step, the second by a whole step, and the third valve (a conspicuous and important addition) by one and a half steps. Various combinations permit, as on modern trumpets, a full chromatic scale over the entire range.

60.0 cm. incl. mouthpiece. Bell dia. 16.0-16.8 cm. Musikinstrumenten Museum des Staatlichen Instituts f. Musikforschung-Preussischer Kultur-besitz, Berlin, 3104.

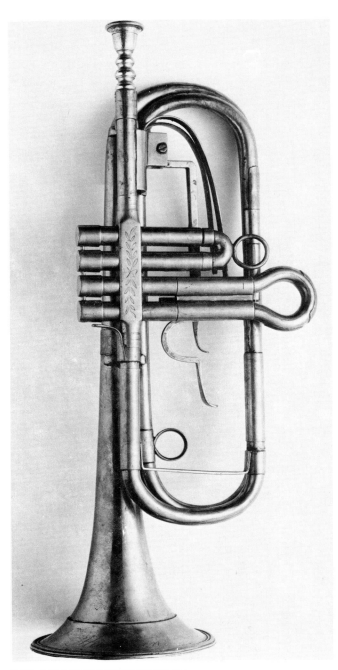

269. VALVE TRUMPET IN F

Andreas Barth, Munich (. . .1835-1868)

This handsome trumpet is later than the preceding two and uses two Vienna valves, a type requiring double pistons and therefore easily recognized. The two levers are depressed to move the valves and are coupled to heavy leaf springs that return the valve to normal position afterward. The instrument is held in what would seem to us an upside-down position, with the loops at the ends of valves uppermost. Again, the first valve lowers pitch by a half-step and the second by a whole step.

L. 38.5 cm. Bell dia. 12.0 cm. Mouthpiece not original. Städt. Musikinstrumentensammlung, Munich, 53/15.

270. VALVE TRUMPET IN B♭

C. F. Schmidt, Weimar (. . .1888-1900. . .)

circa 1890

This is a marvellous instrument, beautifully made, nicely balanced, with a remarkable valve action. It is similar to those used today in European orchestras, where rotary valves are still very much preferred. Schmidt was a well-known maker, especially of horns, many of which are still in use today. The first valve on this instrument lowers the pitch of the instrument to A.

L. 49.4 cm. Bell dia. 13.35 cm. Musikinstrumenten des Staatlichen Instituts f. Musikforschung-Preussischer Kulturbesitz, Berlin, 4140.

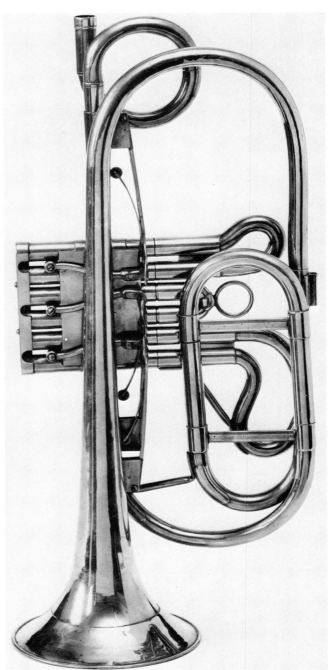

271. CORNET IN B♭

Charles Pace, London (. . .1830-1850. . .)

circa 1840

Pace was an important London maker and made virtually every kind of brass instrument and, incongruously, at least two bassoons. The valves of this instrument are the slim piston type that bear Stölzel's name (and were actually used on cheaper instruments well into the present century), in which the lower portion of the cylindrical valve casing serves as part of the actual windway. Lying horizontally across the left side of the instrument is a clapper key for facilitating various trills. The instrument is provided with crooks for playing in F, G, and Ab, as well as its basic Bb pitch.

Brass with nickel silver mounts. L. 25.0 cm. Bell dia. 11.5 cm. Victoria and Albert Museum, London, W.20-1939.

272. CORNET IN C

C.A. Müller, Mainz (. . .1824-1860. . .)

circa 1860

Levers are used here as on No. 269 to operate the Vienna valves, but on this instrument there are three valves and therefore three separate levers. The instrument would be played in an upside-down position; that is, with the coiled tubing held *above* the mouthpiece-bell axis.

L. 46.0 cm. Bell dia. 12.0 cm. Museum für Hamburgische Geschichte, Hamburg, 1928.370.

273. CORNET IN B♭

Graves & Company, Boston
Samuel Graves, Jr. (1794-1878)

circa 1860

19th century American brass makers show a special fondness for "over the shoulder" and up-turned bell designs, which were intended to project more sound to the troops behind and in front of the marching band. The overall form of this cornet is unabashedly amusing, in my opinion, not only because of the similarity to Dizzy Gillespie's special trumpet circa 1950. The rotary valves seen here are manipulated by string action, still used today on many "French" horns. Graves and Company is discussed briefly under No. 276.

Brass. L. 25.5 cm. H. in playing position 36.25 cm. Bell dia. 12.65 cm.
Yale University, Collection of Musical Instruments, New Haven, 397.

274. CORNET

Joseph Higham, Manchester (1818-1883)

This lovely cornet has rotary valves like No. 273 but they are moved by rods rather than string, the rods moving up and down in outer sleeves that could be mistaken for valve casings but are not. This instrument has a number of crooks and shanks for pitch alteration, as well as an ivory mouthpiece, which on a 19th century brass is quite unusual. The handsome case is of interest in its own right.

36.2 cm. with mouthpiece and longer of two lead pipes. Division of Musical Instruments, Smithsonian Institution, Washington, D.C., 76.27.

275. CORNET IN E♭

John Shaw, Inventor (...1824-1838...)
John Kohler, Maker (...1790-1870?)

circa 1850?

Disc valves are the most interesting feature of this marvellous instrument and are described thus by Bessaraboff: "The 'disc valves', as they were called by the inventor, consisted of two brass discs each, one stationary and one rotary. The stationary disc was affixed to the main tubing of the instrument in such wise that its plane was perpendicular to the axis of the main tube. It also had an additional tube (valve-crook) attached to it. This stationary disc had four holes...The rotating disc had also four holes, connected in pairs by two short lengths of tubing...The disc valves were discarded because of difficulties in keeping them air tight." The rotating disc was moved by rod action through a sleeve, as on the preceding instrument. On top of the bell in front of the three finger buttons are two patent levers used for trills, as on No. 271, but both levers are connected to a single tone hole, giving one the choice of trilling with the right thumb or the right little finger.

L. 35.3 cm. Bell dia. 12.6 cm. Museum of Fine Arts, Boston, 17.1986.

276. KEYED BUGLE IN E♭

Graves & Company, Winchester, New Hampshire
Samuel Graves, Jr. (1794-1878)

circa 1840?

On the eve of Stölzel's invention of valves, woodwind-like keys were added to both the trumpet and cornet in order to provide the desperately needed, missing pitches (see Nos. 200 and 201). The keyed bugle enjoyed a much longer and useful life, which I always found very difficult to understand until in 1978 I heard the instrument played by a young American brass player and scholar, Ralph T. Dudgeon, who has made a special study of it. Far from the honks and wheezes that most of us produce on the odd occasion when we come upon a keyed bugle, Mr. Dudgeon is a virtuoso player in whose hands the instrument is capable of as much as any trumpet or cornet, past or present. This is not an exaggeration, but once again proves that we cannot make judgments of an early instrument until one of us has put aside his modern instrument and concentrated for a considerable period on the old.

Copper body with brass trim. Nine brass keys. L. 48.2 cm. Bell dia. 10.7 cm. Yale University, Collection of Musical Instruments, New Haven, 180.

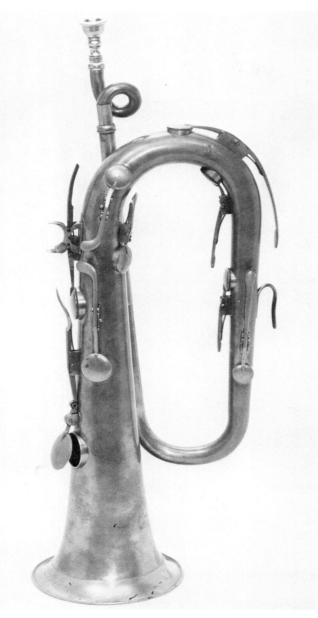

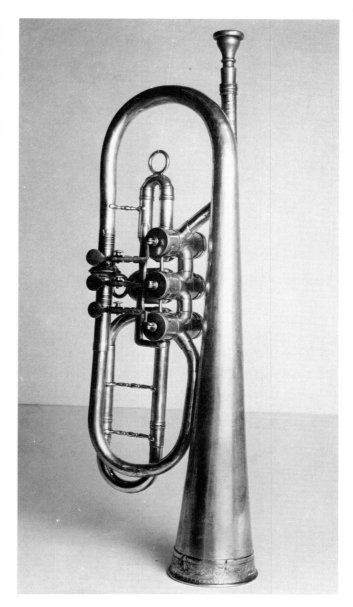

277. KEYED BUGLE IN B♭

Graves & Company, Winchester, New Hampshire
Samuel Graves, Jr. (1794-1878)

This lower-pitched keyed bugle is the other model that received widespread use. Graves & Company is one of the earliest American firms of brass and woodwind makers, and was located until 1850 in the lovely, sleepy, peaceful little town of Winchester, on the banks of the Ashuelot River in southern New Hampshire, which river powered the "factory's" tools. Dr. Robert E. Eliason is the author of a definitive monograph about the firm, listed in the bibliography. After 1850 the company briefly relocated in Boston (No. 273)

Copper, with brass trim. Nine brass keys. 48.7 cm. with Bb crook. Bell dia. 14.0 cm. Division of Musical Instruments, Smithsonian Institution, Washington, D.C., 237,754.

278. FLUGELHORN IN C

Carl Wilhelm Moritz, Berlin (1811-1855)
1842 or 1843

Johann Gottfried Moritz (1777-1840) was an important inventor and brass maker in Berlin, whose son Carl Wilhelm succeeded him, establishing a firm that lasted until 1955 when the last family-president died. The development of modern brass instruments is very much intwined with this family, beginning with Johann Gottfried's invention of the important "Berliner pumpen" (valve) in 1833, three examples of which are seen on this *flugelhorn*. The latter term applies to a valved bugle, built in various keys of which sopranos in Bb or C like this one were most common. This particular instrument is the sort made for use in cavalry bands in the German and Austrian armies, deliberately heavy and very rugged.

L. 43.5 cm. Bell dia. 12.8 cm. Musikinstrumenten Museum des Staatlichen Instituts f. Musikforschung-Preussischer Kulturbesitz, Berlin, 3096.

279. VALVE TROMBONE

Bell by Dominico Grigoletti,
Klagenfurt, dated 1678

Grigoletti is known only by one trombone, which of course would have been the slide type to begin with. In the 19th century, however, its original bell was fitted to a valve trombone with three Vienna-type valves. The strut connecting bell and upper U-bend is proof that fusion was carried out by a skilled brass workman. It is difficult to believe that anything about the bell's playing qualities could be so special, but someone obviously thought this one was worth the effort required to recycle it. Perhaps this example will deter the visitor to *The Look of Music* from giving an older instrument to the junk man.

Overall L. 104.5 cm. Bell dia. 18.3 cm. Städt. Musikinstrumentensammlung, Munich, 41/322.

282. BASS TROMBONE IN F

Anton Betzenhammer, Munich
(1839-1872. . .)

Dated 1872

This massive bass trombone has a slide handle similar to that on Isaac Ehe's Renaissance bass, No. 22, to enable the player to reach the lower positions. It would seem to be a very large bore instrument, especially as it progresses beyond the slide. Trombonists will not miss the unusual fact that there is also a strut or stay half way down the slide, no doubt because of the unusually long span and weight.

Overall L. 138.0 cm. Bell dia. 22.2 cm. Städt. Musikinstrumentensammlung, Munich, 40/40.

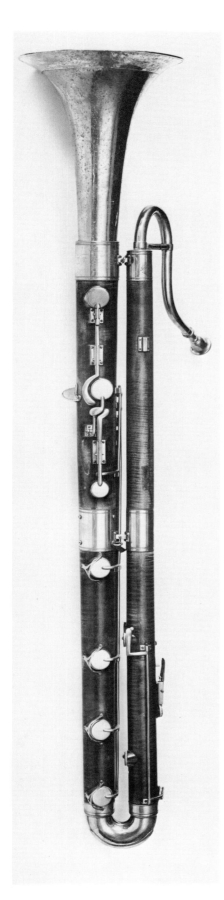

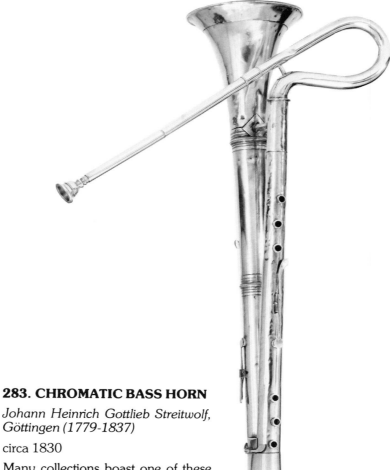

283. CHROMATIC BASS HORN

Johann Heinrich Gottlieb Streitwolf, Göttingen (1779-1837)

circa 1830

Many collections boast one of these handsome instruments that bear the inscription, "Invented and Manufactured by Streitwolf in Göttingen". It is a transitional instrument between the serpent (which for all this time — from the Renaissance to the 19th century — had been the closest thing to a real brass bass, or woodwind bass but for bassoons and bass shawms) and the tuba, which came into being with the invention of valves. Streitwolf attempted to place the tone holes in their acoustically correct positions but in Baines' opinion, the result is a poorer tone than the improved serpents of the time that Streitwolf was attempting to replace. This model has eleven keys and is pitched in Bb.

Maple body with brass bell and U-bend at bottom. Ivory mouthpiece. Eleven brass keys. H. 125.0 cm. Bell dia. 24.0 cm. Museum für Hamburgische Geschichte, Hamburg, 1898.124.

284. ENGLISH BASS HORN IN C

Louis Alexandre Frichot, London (1760-1825)

Here is another attempt, prior to the development of the tuba, to create a brass bass to replace the serpent. Frichot himself was a famous serpent player who fled to London at the outbreak of the French Revolution and reestablished himself there as a performer. He was living in London when he designed this instrument, which may have been made for him by George Astor (see No. 180). At least one similar instrument exists with Astor's label inscribed instead of Frichot's. Eventually he was able to return to France, where he continued to produce (or have produced) a similar bass horn that was there called a "serpent Anglais".

H. 89.0 cm. Bell dia. 17.0 cm. Brass. Four keys. Museum of Fine Arts, Boston, 17.1956.

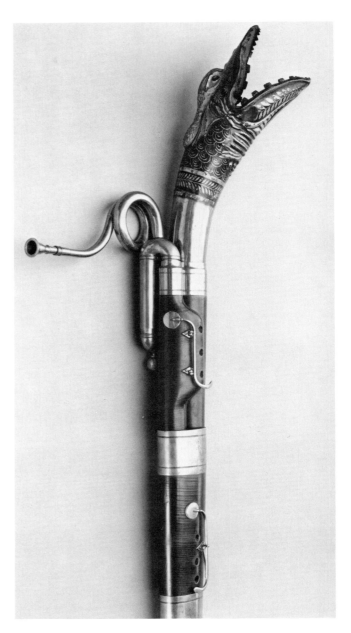

285. TENOR HORN IN B♭

Anonymous

circa 1840

There would seem to be no limit to the variety of form and shapes seen in 19th century brass. This particular design is not often seen. It has the same pitch as the common trombone but with conical bore and three Vienna valves activated by finger buttons on rods. The valves and the contours of the tubing are much nicer than the shape of the bell.

H. 92.0 cm. Bell dia. 21.0 cm. Mouthpiece made of horn. Museum für Hamburgische Geschichte, Hamburg, 1928.375.

286. RUSSIAN BASSOON

Sautermeister & Müller, Lyon
Francois Sautermeister (. . .1809-1830. . .)

circa 1840

This is not a true bassoon - it has a cup mouthpiece - and has no known Russian connection. It has another redesign of the traditional serpent, given bassoon form in this instance by the twin-drilled boot joint with a U-bend at the bottom, with separate sections arising from that. The fanciful bell is often seen on 19th century brasses intended for bands, mainly to entertain onlookers during parades. Some such instruments have a large metal tongue soldered inside the dragon's mouth. This specimen may have possessed a tongue originally.

Tiger maple with brass mounts and three brass keys. Overall L 103.5 cm. School of Music, University of Victoria, 1971-8.

287. SOPRANO SAXHORN IN B♭

Henry Distin, London (. . .1820-1868. . .)

circa 1850

The saxhorn is Sax's most important invention after the saxophone, and precedes the latter by only a year or so. The term "bugle" is used for the family of brass with a medium wide conical bore, with or without valves. While similar horns of every shape and size had previously existed, Sax combined their various features and standardized their design, producing a family of nine valved bugles. While many others claimed in and out of court to have preceded Sax in creating such an instrument, few disputed that his was significantly better. Nomenclature is still a serious problem today, even with the present instrument. Some will point out (correctly) that saxhorns are *upright,* as with Nos. 288 and 289, but Sax himself made some like this model. Distin, who championed Sax throughout his career, shows horizontal soprano saxhorns in his catalogue of 1849, though not with rotary valves. Others would say that this is simply a cornet, and not find much opposition. In any case, this example is a very beautiful instrument.

Inscription: *No. 1105 Henry Distin Maker 31 Cranbourne St. Leicester Square London.*

Nickel silver over brass. Overall L. 34.3 cm. without shank or mouthpiece. Royal Ontario Museum, Toronto, 968.340.

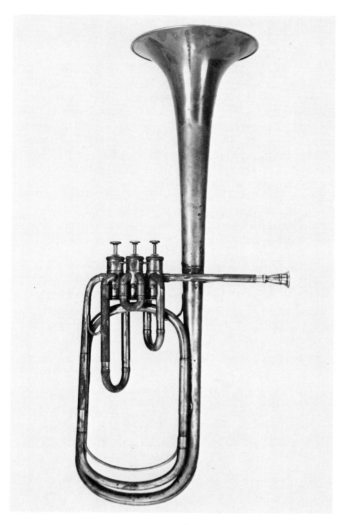

288. ALTO SAXHORN IN E♭

Bartsch, Paris (. . .1837-1855. . .)

This upright form is the characteristic one for saxhorns, one important reason being to permit the tube leading from the mouthpiece to reach the valves as quickly as possible, so that upon leaving the valves the tube may begin its gradual (therefore "conical") expansion, which is an essential factor in producing the mellow sound (as opposed to the trumpet and trombone's "brilliant" sound) that is characteristic of all members of the bugle family. The valves of this instrument are the short, stubby, "Berliner pumpen" (valve) seen earlier on No. 278 and to be seen as well on No. 290.

H. 68.0 cm. Bell dia. 18.2 cm. Bate Collection, Oxford, 661.

289. BARITONE SAXHORN IN B♭

Adolphe Sax, Paris (1814-1894)

The earliest saxhorns made by Sax himself had Berlin valves, according to Bevan, which he copied from two instruments bought from Moritz, the important Berlin maker and inventor (Nos. 278 and 290). It may be, therefore, that this is one of the earlier saxhorns. Bevan makes an important point: "Here was a range of instruments pitched from b♭' down to BBB, alternately in Eb and Bb. Their relative proportions were fairly constant. . .and consequently their timbres matched. This has been singled out as Sax's really important discovery — that the profile of the instrument confers its timbre." Thus whatever else Sax accomplished or borrowed in designing the saxhorn, he gave the entire family a uniform bore, thereby creating matched quality of sound throughout the wide range, which a motley assortment of similar types had not had before.

Inscription: *Adolphe Sax, Fteur, Brevete, de la Mson Milre de l'Empereur (Maison militaire)*, 50 Rue St. Georges a Paris, No. 32900. Saxhorn Baryton en Sib.

H. 78.0 cm. Bell 20.0 cm. Bate Collection, Oxford, 662.

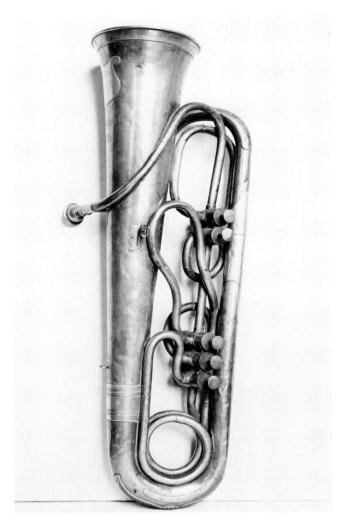

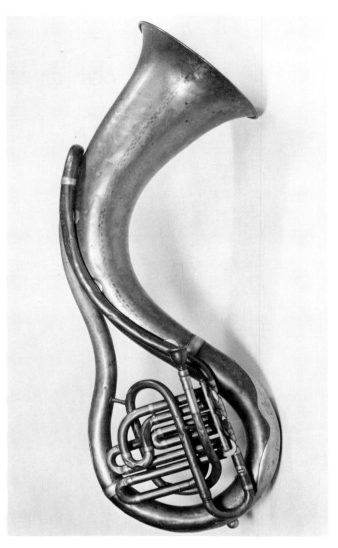

290. BASS TUBA IN F

Johann Gottfried Moritz, Berlin (1777-1840)

This instrument is one of the very earliest bass tubas made and is probably the best known through photographs in a number of major books. The significance of the Moritz family is cited under No. 278, but the maker of this instrument was by far the most important member of the family as well as the founder of the business. He is the inventor of the "Berliner pumpen" seen on this instrument as well as on Nos. 278, 288, and 289, and made many additional contributions to brass development as well. The excellent new book by Clifford Bevan, *The Tuba Family*, gives more information about Moritz and his achievements than has been known to this time.

The lower three valves here are the main set and are arranged as on modern brass, the first valve lowering pitch by a whole step, the second by a half step, and the third by one and a half steps. The upper valves apparently transpose the instrument into Eb and C.

Brass, with German silver fittings. Overall H. 84.1 cm. Bell dia. 19.3 cm. Musikinstrumenten Museum des Staatlichen Instituts f. Musikforschung-Preussischer Kulturbesitz, Berlin, 4456.

291. BASS TUBA IN E♭

Louis Schreiber, New York (1827-1868. . .)

This "over-the-shoulder" tuba is engraved "PATENT L. SCHREIBER SEPT. 12, 1865, NY, USA", which would seem to imply that this maker had arrived in the United States by that date from Germany. He was born in Coblenz in 1827. Not much more seems to be known of him, but there are other tantalizing bits of conflicting information: for example, a Russian patent issued in 1869 and the existence by the late 1860s of a "Schreiber Cornet Manufacturing Company" in New York that seems to have patented various improvements including string-drive for rotary valves. Another bass tuba by Schreiber with three rotary valves is said to be in a collection in Nazareth, Pennsylvania. The "over-the-shoulder" design is explained under No. 273.

Brass, with German or nickel silver fittings. Three rotary valves. Overall L 101.65 cm. Royal Ontario Museum, Toronto, 913.4.71.

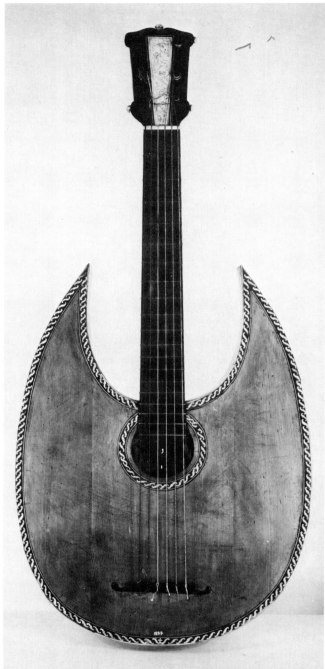

292. PORTUGUESE GUITAR

Rosa & Caldeira, Lisbon (. . .1899. . .)

This is a kind of cittern (flat back, wire strings, frets), of which several other varieties were seen earlier (Nos. 203-205). In place of string tighteners using a watch key, the present instrument has individual knobs that tighten each string of the six courses. This cittern was popular in Spain and France as well as in the country for which it was named.

Belly of fir(?), back and ribs of rosewood. L 71.5 cm. W 30.0 cm. 19 frets. Musée Instrumental, Brussels, 2494.

293. GUITAR

Gennaro Fabricatore, Naples (. . .1817. . .)

Dated 1817

Victor Mahillon described this instrument as shaped like a *croissant*. In today's terminology it is a cut-away model, with symmetrical cuts being made in either side of the exceptionally long fingerboard. It has the six single strings to which the guitar was reduced in the 18th century to make it more accessible to amateurs.

Overall L 91.0 cm. W 41.0 cm. 19 brass frets. Musée Instrumental, Brussels, 1537.

294. GUITAR

Johann Anton Stauffer, Kaschau (. . .1805-1843. . .)

Jalovec gives the above dates and says that Johann Anton made better violins than his father, Johann Georg, but not such good guitars. The son served as assistant to his father in Vienna (where his father invented a bowed guitar that attracted some attention), and then relocated in Hungary. The nicely designed pegboard is quite unusual.

Spruce belly, mahogany ribs and back. Ivory fingerboard and edging on both belly and back. Overall L 87.8 cm. Bouts 23.4 cm., 17.3 cm. and 29.3 cm. Musikhistorisk Museet og Carl Claudius' Samling, Copenhagen, C-175.

295. BANJO

Fred Mather, New York City

mid-19th century?

The banjo is believed to have been brought from Africa during the slave trade, and carried thence to Europe (or at least to England) by the famed Christy Minstrels. In its simplest and earliest form it consists of strings stretched across a vellum-covered frame, nailed down with brass tacks. Eventually threaded tensioning rods were added to tighten a wooden hoop around which the vellum was stretched. This example is strung with gut, although wire often was used beginning in the 19th century. The short, fifth string on the bass side is a drone string usually tuned to the dominant. Scordatura is common on all strings. Frets are common but missing here.

L circa 86.0 cm. W circa 30.5 cm. Division of Musical Instruments, Smithsonian Institution, Washington, D.C., 207.888.

296. CONCERT ZITHER

Georg Tiefenbrunner, Munich (1812-1880)

dated 1845

This is the largest size of three standard zithers and is the "Salzburg model" as opposed to the "Mittenwald", which labels have to do with external profile. The instrument is especially identified with the Bavarian and Austrian Alps, as well as with the theme song from the film *The Third Man*. There are four melody strings to the left, over the fretted fingerboard, while to the right are accompaniment and bass strings, 27 in all. On this fairly early instrument all strings are tuned by wrest pins, but later models use "machines" to tune the melody strings. The scroll at the top is a vestige of the earlier *scheitholt*, from which the folk zither is descended.

L 154.5 cm. W 30.3 cm. Musée Instrumental, Brussels, 1516.

297. FRENCH LYRE

Boulan, Arras

Dated 17??

The venerable Grecian lyre arose from the grave in the 18th century to become a guitar-like plaything for fashionable ladies for nearly a century. Known as the lyre-guitar, it belongs to the same age that enjoyed Nos. 203 to 205. Its shape made it extremely unwieldy but there was enormous variety in the outline and surface decoration of the body: it was probably enjoyed as much as a room decoration as for its music. This particular specimen had seven wire strings.

L 78.0 cm. W 39.0 cm. Musée Instrumental, Brussels, 3180.

298. HARP

*Sébastian & Pierre Érard, London
(1752-1831) (1796-1855)*

This is the "Gothic model" of Érard harp that nephew Pierre brought out in 1836. It has 46 strings tuned C-g'''' and the standard seven pedals. It was Sébastian who made the first piano constructed in France, a square, but his activities were transferred to London at the time of the Revolution. He eventually returned to Paris and began making both grand pianos and harps, although he maintained a London branch. His double action harp was introduced in 1810 and was known as the "Greek model" because of style of ornamentation. Pierre eventually succeeded his uncle and made notable advances in his own right.

H 174.6 cm. Serial number 5634. Private Collection, Victoria.

299. VIOLIN

Jean Baptiste Vuillaume, Paris (1798-1875)

Dated 1871

Few luthiers in the history of violin making have come closer to equalling the great instruments of Cremona than Jean Baptiste Vuillaume, and few have fooled experts and amateurs alike more often than Vuillaume with his copies of the older makers. He truly must have cursed the Italians ten times a day, for so good was he (as he well knew), that he had to stand constant comparison. Always, if only sentimentally, he was placed second. An interesting sidelight concerns his one-time practice of baking the wood in order to make it appear much older; the violins thus treated have apparently all deteriorated. As his success and fame increased, be it to his eternal credit, his standards rose as well and it became more and more difficult for any expert to distinguish his from the work of one of the earlier masters. When he began to make celli, he was equally and perhaps even more successful. He is said to have completed 3000 instruments in all. This instrument is a copy of a Jos. Guarnerius and bears the label *"Jean Baptiste Vuillaume a Paris, 3 rue Demoues-Ternes."*

L 59.9 cm. Body L 35.5 cm. Bouts 17.0 cm., 11.5 cm. and 21.0 cm. Depth circa 6.0 cm. Musée Instrumental du Conservatoire de Paris, E. 883, C.49.

300. VIOLIN

Jean Baptiste Vuillaume, Paris (1798-1875)

This is one of Vuillaume's standard models, and for a long time it was assumed from dozens or perhaps hundreds of such instruments that Gaspar Duifforprugcar, whose "label" it bears, was the first known maker of violins, a distinction of no small importance. The decoration of this violin is a composite of Renaissance devices, from the man's head atop the pegbox (which was said to be Gaspar himself), to the inlaid scene of a medieval city on the lower back, to the carved leaf at the top of the back, to the legend inscribed on the ribs, "I was alive in the wood. I was killed by the cruel axe; living I was silent, dead I sing sweetly." Such "early" violins do not seem to have had as much effort put into them as Vuillaume devoted to copies of Stradivari and the other Cremona makers, but they did indeed mislead everyone for a long time. For reference to another Vuillaume copy, see No. 133.

L. 62.55 cm. Royal Ontario Museum, Toronto, 948.73.1.

301. VIOLINO-HARPA

Thomas Zach, Vienna (1812-1892)

Dated 1873

"A hideous attempt to increase tone through soundbox enlargement," is the way this instrument is explained by Anthony Baines in *European and American Musical Instruments*. Other, less hallucinatory modifications have been tried experimentally — removing the sharp corners on either side of the middle bouts, or rounding the edges completely of both the belly and back, for example — in quest of more of something or other. Whether or not something new will do something better in the future, nothing thus far has threatened the supremacy of the Cremona models. They *work*.

L circa 58.0 cm. W 36.0 cm. Musée Instrumental, Brussels, 1359.

302. SQUARE PIANO

Astor & Horwood, London

circa 1820

The Astor and Horwood partnership developed from George Astor's woodwind making, after he added other instruments including pianos to his repertoire. There is little doubt that well before this point, in fact, the Astor firm was acting as a dealer and distributor of every kind of instrument, sometimes stamped with the actual maker's name and sometimes with only Astor's, with or without the unicorn-head trademark that he (and it would seem, others as well) used some of the time. This is a very handsome piano in Regency style. No longer of musical value, supposedly, a great number of squares have suffered conversion to writing desks or sideboards.

Cuban mahogany, rosewood, and ebony; ivory and brass inlay. Compass FF-c''''. L 171.1 cm. Depth 63.5 cm. H 87.0 cm. Montreal Museum of Fine Arts, 960.Df.3.

303. SQUARE PIANO

Alpheus Babcock, Philadelphia (. . .1790-1837. . .)

circa 1835

The main importance of Babcock and of this piano is its cast iron frame. The logic of using a cast iron frame had been long apparent, but there was also resistance to it because of prejudice toward the introduction of metal into an otherwise traditionally all-wood musical instrument. To meet the new craving for powerful tone and brilliance, there was really only one answer — an iron frame that could resist the increased tension imposed on the piano strings. This was first achieved by Babcock, even though Broadwood and others had used metal pieces, but never entire frames, to try to achieve the same goal. Babcock was also among the first to promote over-stringing (see No. 304). Along with other, more important contributions of a technical sort, Babcock managed to emphasize attractive proportion and design in his pianos. He originally worked in Boston, but later moved to Philadelphia, where he made this piano and others for an established local piano maker, William Swift's Piano Manufactory.

L 181.6 cm. Depth 76.2 cm. H 92.7 cm. Compass FF-f''''. Two pedals. Division of Musical Instruments Smithsonian Institution, Washington, D.C., 315,690.

304. GRAND PIANO

Steinway & Sons, New York
Heinrich Engelhard Steinweg (1797-1871)

1857

The Steinway saga is one of the great American success stories. The father had won prizes as a master piano-maker in Europe before he and two sons immigrated to New York, where they opened their own shop in 1853 and won their first major award a year later. This is certainly one of their first grands, a rare example of a straight-strung Steinway grand. Overstringing meant having the longer bass strings pass diagonally above the remaining strings, a better utilization of space : in this grand, however, one can see that all the strings are parallel from the keyboard to the far end.

Overall L 245.0 cm. Overall W 139.5 cm. H with top closed 100.0 cm. Compass AAA-a''''. Serial no. 1199. Division of Musical Instruments, Smithsonian Institution, Washington, D.C., 74.6.

305. SQUARE PIANO

Theodore A. Heintzman (1819-1899)

Dated 1854

This square piano was built by Theodore A. Heintzman, the founder of one of Canada's most prominent firms of piano manufacture. The company is still operated by Heintzman's descendants.

Serial No. 446
W 178 cm. H 87 cm. D 76 cm. Heintzman Limited, Ontario.

BIBLIOGRAPHY

General

American Musical Instrument Society *Journal,* 1975-
Baines, Anthony C., *European and American Musical Instruments,* New York
     1966, editor, *Musical Instruments through the Ages,* London 1961
Benade, Arthur H., *Fundamentals of Musical Acoustics,* New York & London,
     1976
Bessaraboff, Nicholas, *Ancient European Musical Instruments,* Cambridge
     (USA) 1941
Bragard, Roger, and de Hen, Ferdinand, *Musical Instruments in Art and
     History,* London 1968
Buchner, Alexander, *Musical Instruments through the Ages,* London 1961
Galpin, Canon Francis W., *Old English Instruments of Music,* 4th edition,
     London 1965
Galpin Society *Journal,* London 1948-
Harrison, Frank L., and Rimmer, Joan *European Musical Instruments,* London
     1964
Jenkins, Jean, *International Directory of Musical Instrument Collections,*
     Buren, 1977
Kinsky, Georg, *A History of Music in Pictures,* New York 1937
Lichtenwanger, William, et al, *A Survey of Musical Instrument Collections* in
     the *United States and Canada,* Ann Arbor 1974
Marcuse, Sibyl, *Musical Instruments, A comprehensive Dictionary,* New York
     1964
Sachs, Curt, *The History of Musical Instruments,* New York 1940
     Real Lexikon der Musikinstrumente, Berlin 1913, revised edition 1964
Winternitz, Emanuel, *Musical Instruments of the Western World,* London 1966

Music Dictionaries

Apel, Willi, *Harvard Dictionary of Music,* 2nd edition, Cambridge 1969
Blom, Eric, editor, *Grove's Dictionary of Music and Musicians,* 5th edition,
     London 1954
Blume, F., editor, *Musik in Geschichte und Gegenwart,* Kassel 1949-
Sadie, S., editor, *The New Grove* (Grove's Dictionary of Music & Musicians,
     6th edition)

General Historical Eras

Medieval and Renaissance:

Crane, Frederick, *Extant Medieval Musical Instruments: A Provisional
     Catalogue by Type,* Iowa City 1972
Montagu, Jeremy, *The World of Medieval & Renaissance Musical Instruments,*
     London 1976
Munrow, David, *Instruments of the Middle Ages and Renaissance,* London
     1976

Praetorius, Michael, *Syntagma Musicum* Vol. 2 De Organographia, Wolfenbüttel 1619, (Engish translation) New York 1962

Baroque and Classical:

Montagu, Jeremy, *The World of Baroque and Classical Musical Instruments*, London
Carse, Adam, *The Orchestra in the XVIIIth Century*, Cambridge 1940
  The Orchestra from Beethoven to Berlioz, Cambridge 1948

Wind Instruments

Baines, Anthony, *Woodwind Instruments and Their History*, revised edition, New York 196
  Brass Instruments, Their History and Development, London 1976
Bate, Philip A.T., *The Flute*, London 1969
  The Oboe, 3rd edition, London 1975
  The Trumpet and Trombone, London 1966
Boehm, Theobald, *The Flute and Flute Playing*, translated by D.C. Miller, New York 1960
Brüchle & Janetzky, *Pictorial History of the Horn from the Bronze Age to the Present Day*, Tutzing 1796
Carse, Adam, *Musical Wind Instruments*, reprint, New York 1965
Fitzpatrick, Horace, *The Horn and Horn Playing. . .from 1680 to 1830*, New York 1970
Haine Malou, *Adolphe Sax, sa vie, son oeuvre, ses instruments de musique*, Brussels, 1980
Hotteterre, Jacques, *Principles of the Flute, Recorder, and Oboe*, Amsterdam 1728, translated by Lasocki, London 1968
Hunt, Edgar, *The Recorder and Its Music*, revised edition, London 1962
Jansen, Will, *The Basoon: Its History, Construction, Makers, Players, and Music*, Büren 1978-
Kroll, Oskar, *The Clarinet*, New York 1968
Langwill, Lyndesay G., *An Index of Musical Wind Isntrument Makers*, sixth edition, Edinburgh 1980
  The Bassoon and Contrabassoon, London 1965
Morley-Pegge, R., *the French Horn*, London 1960
Nickel, Ekkehart, *Der Holzblasinstrumentenbau in der Freien Reichsstadt Nürnberg*, Munich 1971
Quantz, Johann Joachim, *On Playing the Flute*, translation by Edward R. Reilly, London 1966 (of *Versuch Einer Anweisung*, Berlin 1752)
Rendall, F.G., revised Bate, P.A.T., *The Clarinet*, 3rd edition, London 1971
Saam, Josef, *Das Bassetthorn*, Mainz, 1971
Smithers, Don L., *History of the Baroque Trumpet before 1721*, London 1973
Ventzke, Karl, Die Boehmflöte, Frankfurt 1966
Young, Phillip T., *2500 Historical Woodwind Instruments, An Inventory of the Major Collections*, New York 1980

String Instruments

Bachmann, Werner, *The Origin of Bowing,* translation by N. Deane, London 1969

Bellow, Lexander, *The Illustrated History of the Guitar,* New York 1970

Boyden, David D., *The History of Violin Playing from Its Origins to 1761,* London 1965

  The Hill Collection of Musical Instruments, Oxford 1969

Cooper, Robert S., *Lute Construction,* Savannah 1963

Cowling, Elizabeth, *The Cello,* London 1975

Dolmetsch, Natalie, *The Viola da Gamba,* 3rd edition, London 1975

Harwood, Ian, *A Brief History of the Lute,* Lute Society 1975

Hayes, Gerald R., *The Viols and Other Bowed Instruments,* reprint, New York 1969

Hellwig, Günther, *Joachim Tielke,* Frankfurt am Main 1980

Hill, W.H. et al, *Antonio Stradivari, His Life and Work,* London, reprint New York 1967

  The Violin Makers of the Guarneri Family, London 1931

The Lute Society *Journal,* London, 1959-

Lütgendorff, W.L. von, Die Geigen- und Lautenmacher. Frankfurt am Main 1922

Nelson, Sheila, *the Violin and Viola,* London 1972

Panum, Hortense, *Stringed Instruments of the Middle Ages,* translated J. Pulver, London 1941

Rensch, Roslyn, *The Harp,* London 1969

Retford, William C., *Bows and Bow Makers,* London 1964

Van der Straeten, Edward, *History of the Violin,* Vol. I & II, London 1933

Vannes, Rene, *Dictionnaire Universel des Luthiers,* Brussels 1951 & 1959

Keyboard Instruments

Audsley, George Ashdown, *The Art of Organ Building,* New York 1965

Boalch, Donald H., *Makers of the Harpsichord and Clavichord 1440-1840,* revised edition, Oxford 1974

Harding, Rosamond, *The Piano Forte, its History Traced to the Great Exhibition of 1851,* Cambridge 1933

Hollis, Helen Rice, *The Piano,* London 1975

Hubbard, Frank, *Three Centuries of Harpsichord Making,* Cambridge (USA) 1965

James, Philip, *Early Keyboard Instruments,* London 1930

Russell, Raymond, *The Harpsichord and Clavichord,* 2nd edition, London 1973

Summer, William Leslie, *The Organ,* 3rd revised edition, London 1962

Percussion Instruments

Blades, James, *Percussion Instruments and Their History,* 2nd edition,
London 1975 and Montagu, Jeremy, *Early Percussion Instruments,*
London 1976
Peinkofer, Karl, and Tannigel, Fritz, *Handbook of Percussion Instruments,*
New York 1976

The Major Catalogues of Instrument Collections, Mainly of Recent Date

Antwerp: *Stad Antwerpen Oudheidkundige Musea Vleeshuis, Vol. 5,
Muziekinstrumenten,* Antwerp, n.d.
Berlin: *Sammlung alter Musikinstrumente dei der Staatliche Hoschschule für
Musik zu Berlin,* Berlin 1922. By Curt Sachs.
Berlin: *Katalog der Streichinstrumente,* by Otto & Adelmann, Berlin 1975
Berlin: *Katalog der Blechblasinstrumente,* by D. Krickeberg & W. Rauch,
Berlin 1976
Boston: *Ancient European Musical Instruments,* by Nicholas Bessaraboff, is a
catalogue of the collection at the Museum of Fine Arts, as of 1941
Brussels: *Catalogue descriptif et analytique du Musee. . .Vol. 1-5,* by Victor
Charles Mahillon, Brussels 1893-1912; reprint 1979
Copenhagen: *Das Musikhistorische Museum zu Kobenhagen . . .* by A.
Hammerich, Copenhagen 1911
(The above museum now incorporates the following once-private
collection)
Copenhagen: *Carl Claudius Sammlung af Gamble Musikinstrumenter,*
Copenhagen 1931
Edinburgh: *The Russell Collection & Other Early Keyboard Instruments in St.
Cecelia's Hall,* University of Edinburgh 1968
Eisenach: *Historische Musikinstrumente im Bachhaus Eisenach,* by Herbert
Heyde, 1976
Florence: *Gli Strumenti Musicali della corte Medicea. . .,* by V. Gai, Florence
1969
Halle: *Händelhaus Katalog,* by Konrad Sasse (full details unknown)
Leipzig: *Flöten,* by Herbert Heyde, a catalogue of flutes and recorders
Musikinstrumenten Museum, Leipzig 1978
Leningrad: *Katalog Sobraniya Muzykalnych Instrumentov,* by G.I.
Blagodatov, Leningrad 1972
London: *Catalogue of Musical Instruments, Victoria & Albert Museum: Non-
Keyboard Instruments* (Vol.II) by Anthony Baines, London 1968
*Catalogue of Musical Instruments, Victoria & Albert Museum: Keyboard
Instruments (Vol. I)* by Raymond Russell, London 1968

Milan: *Museo degli Strumenti Musicali,* by N. & F. Gallini, catalogue of the
collection housed at Castello Sforzesco, Florence 1963

Munich: *Die Blasinstrumente im Deutschen Museum,* by Heinrich Seifers, München 1976

New Haven: *Checklist: Yale Collection of Musical Instruments, Yale University,* by Richard Rephann, 1968

New York: Checklists of several types of instrument now available: by Laurence Libin. Western European Fifes, Piccolos, and Transverse Flutes; Western Europe Flageolets, Recorders, and Tabor Pipes; Viole da Gamba; Bagpipes; European Harps. 1976-   . Metropolitan Museum of Art.

Nürnberg: *Wegweiser durch die Sammlung Historischer Musikinstrumente,* by John Henry van der Meer. Germanisches Nationalmuseum, Nürnberg n.d.

Oxford: *The Hill Collection of Musical Instruments,* by David D. Boyden. Ashmolean Museum, Oxford University 1969

Oxford: *The Bate Collection of historical Wind Instruments,* by Anthony Baines. Faculty of Music, Oxford 1976

Quito, Ecuador: *A Catalogue of the Pedro Traversari Collection of Musical Instruments* by Richard Rephann, 1978

Salzburg: *Die Holzblasinstrumente im Salzburger Museum Carolino Augusteum,* by Kurt Birsak, alzburg 1973

Salzburg: *Die Blechblasinstrumente im Salzburger Museum Carolino Augusteum,* by Kurt Birsak, published as part of the Museum's Jahresschrift 22/1976

Toronto: *Musical Instruments in the Royal Ontario Museum,* by Ladislav Cselenyi, Toronto 1969

Vienna: *Die Sammlung alter Musikinstrumente,* by Julius von Schlosser, Vienna 1922

Vienna: *Katalog der Sammlung alter Musikinstrumente: Teil I: Saitenklaviere,* by Victor Luithlen, Vienna 1966

Washington, D.C.: *The Dayton C. Miller Flute Collection, A Checklist of the Instruments* by Laura E. Gilliam & William Lichtenwanger, Library of Congress, Washington, 1961

Washington, D.C.: *A Checklist of Keyboard Instruments at the Smithsonian Institution,* by Cynthia A. Hoover, Scott Odell, and others. Washington 1967

Vancouver Centennial Museum staff for "The Look of Music"

Project Director:	Robert D. Watt
Project Curator:	Carol E. Mayer
Special Consultant:	Phillip T. Young
Associate Curator:	Ivan W. Sayers
Registrar:	Lesley Moore
Conservators:	Marie N. Challan-Belval
	Roy Waterman
Exhibition Staff:	Victor Lowe
	Chris Holland
	George Nethery
	S. Barrett
	A. Blair
	Heide Didzuhn
	Mary Paddon
	Henry Tabbers
Public Programmes:	Lynette Harper
Concert Coordinator:	Donna Hossack
School Programmes:	Beverley MacPherson
Publicity/Public Relations:	Raymond McAllister
	Elizabeth Kirley
Publications Officer:	June Franklin
Visitor & Security Services:	Kent McFarlane

About the Author

Professor Phillip T. Young of the University of Victoria School of Music in British Columbia, Canada, is one of the world's leading authorities on historical musical instruments. Formerly Executive Officer of The School of Music at Yale University (where he obtained his M.Mus. in performance as a bassoon player), he also holds a B.A. (music major) from Bowdoin College, Maine, and has conducted symphony and chamber orchestras and concert bands. As consultant to Vancouver Centennial Museum for the exhibition *The Look of Music*, Phillip Young visited dozens of museums in Europe and North America, personally selecting and researching the instruments about which he writes in this book.